OFFICIAL SQA PAST PAPERS
WITH ANSWERS

ADVANCED HIGHER

BIOLOGY
2007-2011

2007 EXAM   – page 3
2008 EXAM   – page 29
2009 EXAM   – page 57
2010 EXAM   – page 85
2011 EXAM   – page 115
ANSWER SECTION – page 147

✕SQA

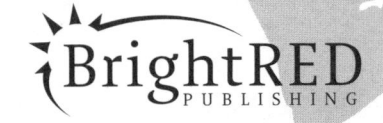

Publisher's Note

We are delighted to bring you the 2011 Past Papers and you will see that we have changed the format from previous editions. As part of our environmental awareness strategy, we have attempted to make these new editions as sustainable as possible.

To do this, we have printed on white paper and bound the answer sections into the book. This not only allows us to use significantly less paper but we are also, for the first time, able to source all the materials from sustainable sources.

We hope you like the new editions and by purchasing this product, you are not only supporting an independent Scottish publishing company but you are also, in the International Year of Forests, not contributing to the destruction of the world's forests.

Thank you for your support and please see the following websites for more information to support the above statement –

www.fsc-uk.org

www.loveforests.com

© Scottish Qualifications Authority
All rights reserved. Copying prohibited. No part of this publication may be reproduced, stored in a retrieval system, or transmitted in any form or by any means, electronic, mechanical, photocopying, recording or otherwise.

First exam published in 2007.
Published by Bright Red Publishing Ltd, 6 Stafford Street, Edinburgh EH3 7AU
tel: 0131 220 5804 fax: 0131 220 6710 info@brightredpublishing.co.uk www.brightredpublishing.co.uk

ISBN 978-1-84948-228-8

A CIP Catalogue record for this book is available from the British Library.

Bright Red Publishing is grateful to the copyright holders, as credited on the final page of the Question Section, for permission to use their material. Every effort has been made to trace the copyright holders and to obtain their permission for the use of copyright material. Bright Red Publishing will be happy to receive information allowing us to rectify any error or omission in future editions.

[BLANK PAGE]

X007/701

NATIONAL
QUALIFICATIONS
2007

MONDAY, 21 MAY
1.00 PM – 3.30 PM

BIOLOGY
ADVANCED HIGHER

SECTION A–Questions 1—25 (25 marks)

Instructions for completion of Section A are given on *Page two*.

SECTIONS B AND C

The answer to each question should be written in ink in the answer book provided. Any additional paper (if used) should be placed inside the front cover of the answer book.

Rough work should be scored through.

Section B (55 marks)

All questions should be attempted. Candidates should note that Question 8 contains a choice.

Question 1 is on Pages 8, 9 and 10. Questions 2, 3 and 4 are on Page 11. Pages 10 and 11 are fold-out pages.

Section C (20 marks)

Candidates should attempt the questions in **one** unit, **either** Biotechnology **or** Animal Behaviour **or** Physiology, Health and Exercise.

SCOTTISH
QUALIFICATIONS
AUTHORITY

Read carefully

1   Check that the answer sheet provided is for **Biology Advanced Higher (Section A)**.

2   For this section of the examination you must use an **HB pencil** and, where necessary, an eraser.

3   Check that the answer sheet you have been given has **your name**, **date of birth**, **SCN** (Scottish Candidate Number) and **Centre Name** printed on it.

    Do not change any of these details.

4   If any of this information is wrong, tell the Invigilator immediately.

5   If this information is correct, **print** your name and seat number in the boxes provided.

6   The answer to each question is **either** A, B, C or D. Decide what your answer is, then, using your pencil, put a horizontal line in the space provided (see sample question below).

7   There is **only one correct** answer to each question.

8   Any rough working should be done on the question paper or the rough working sheet, **not** on your answer sheet.

9   At the end of the exam, put the **answer sheet for Section A inside the front cover of the answer book**.

Sample Question

Which of the following molecules contains six carbon atoms?

A   Glucose

B   Pyruvic acid

C   Ribulose bisphosphate

D   Acetyl coenzyme A

The correct answer is **A**—Glucose.   The answer **A** has been clearly marked in **pencil** with a horizontal line (see below).

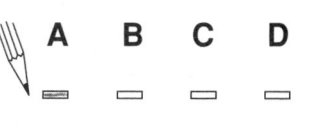

Changing an answer

If you decide to change your answer, carefully erase your first answer and using your pencil, fill in the answer you want. The answer below has been changed to **D**.

SECTION A

All questions in this section should be attempted.

Answers should be given on the separate answer sheet provided.

1. What name is given to the cytoplasmic connections that link adjacent plant cells?

   A   Microvilli

   B   Microfilaments

   C   Plasmodesmata

   D   Middle lamellae

2. The figure below shows the number of cells in a tissue sample at various stages of the cell cycle.

   The mitotic index for this sample is

   A   3

   B   4

   C   25

   D   33.

3. Which line in the table correctly describes the chemical reaction in which a fatty acid is joined to a glycerol?

	Type of reaction	Type of bond formed
A	hydrolysis	ester
B	condensation	glycosidic
C	hydrolysis	glycosidic
D	condensation	ester

4. Which of the following diagrams illustrates a peptide bond?

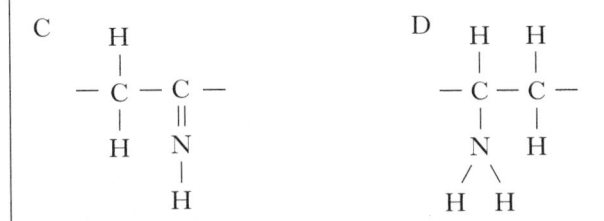

5. The proportion of sugars produced in the breakdown of starch can be measured by the dextrose equivalent (DE). The DE can be calculated as follows:

$$DE = 100 \times \frac{\text{number of glycosidic bonds broken}}{\text{number of glycosidic bonds originally present}}$$

   What is the approximate DE when an amylose molecule is completely digested to maltose?

   A   0·5

   B   1·0

   C   50

   D   100

6. Which of the following describes the structure of cytosine?

   A   A purine base with a single-ring structure

   B   A purine base with a double-ring structure

   C   A pyrimidine base with a single-ring structure

   D   A pyrimidine base with a double-ring structure

[Turn over

7. A diploid cell contains 6×10^9 base pairs of genetic code. Only 4% of this codes for protein.

   How many anticodons does this represent?

   A $2 \cdot 4 \times 10^7$

   B 8×10^7

   C $2 \cdot 4 \times 10^8$

   D 8×10^8

8. To which group of signalling molecules does testosterone belong?

   A   Extracellular hydrophobic

   B   Extracellular hydrophilic

   C   Peptide hormone

   D   Neurotransmitter

9. Enzymes that catalyse the hydrolysis of phosphodiester bonds in genetic material are called

   A   kinases

   B   ligases

   C   ATPases

   D   nucleases.

10. The diagram below shows the effect of isoleucine on the enzyme threonine deaminase.

isoleucine

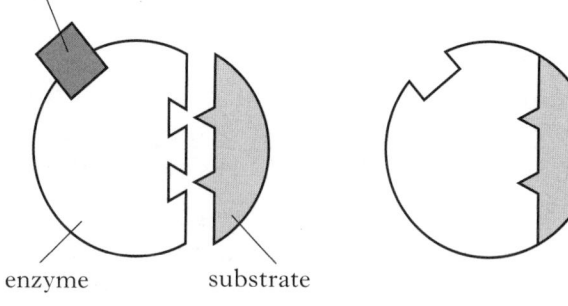

enzyme   substrate

   isoleucine   isoleucine
    present   absent

   In high concentrations, isoleucine acts as

   A   an allosteric inhibitor

   B   an allosteric activator

   C   a competitive inhibitor

   D   a positive modulator.

11. The graph shows the results of an investigation using the enzyme invertase that breaks down sucrose into glucose and fructose. 1 g of sucrose was dissolved in 100 cm^3 water and 2 cm^3 of a 1% invertase solution was added.

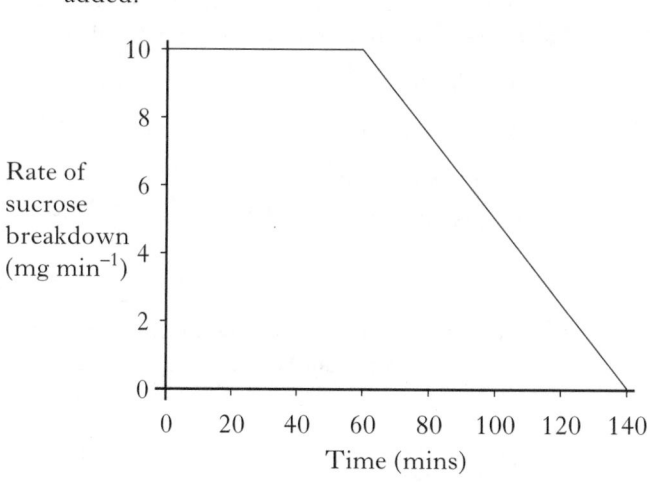

Rate of sucrose breakdown (mg min^{-1})

Time (mins)

   Which of the following conclusions can be drawn from this information?

   A   At 70 minutes exactly half the substrate remains.

   B   Between 0 and 60 minutes the concentration of the substrate remains constant.

   C   At 140 minutes the enzyme is no longer active.

   D   Between 60 and 140 minutes the concentration of the substrate is the limiting factor.

12. The following stages are used to introduce a "foreign" gene into a tomato plant.

   W   Descendent plant cells receive copies of foreign gene.

   X   Foreign gene inserted into plasmid.

   Y   Altered plasmid introduced into cultured plant cells.

   Z   Plasmid isolated from *Agrobacterium tumefaciens*.

   These stages would occur in the order

   A   Y, W, X, Z

   B   Z, X, Y, W

   C   X, Z, W, Y

   D   Z, Y, X, W.

13. Which of the following processes only takes place in autotrophs?

A Assimilation

B Decomposition

C Photosynthesis

D Respiration

14. The number of trophic levels in a food chain is limited because at each level the

A amount of energy decreases

B number of organisms decreases

C biomass decreases

D productivity decreases.

15. In aquatic ecosystems the amount of sunlight absorbed by water increases with depth.

Absorption by seawater is greater than absorption by fresh water.

Which of the following graphs represents the relationship between depth and light intensity in fresh water and seawater?

Key

—————— fresh water

-------- seawater

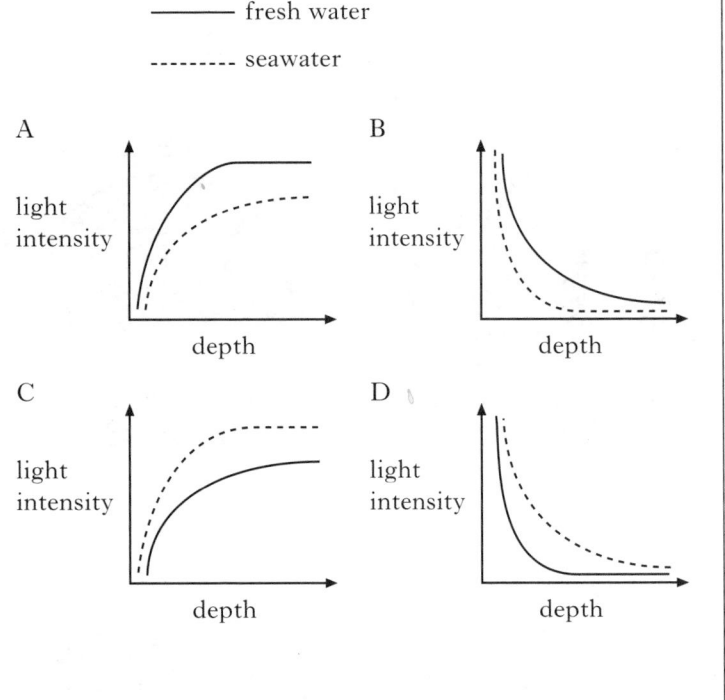

16. In the nitrogen cycle, which of the following bacteria utilises nitrogenase?

A *Rhizobium*

B *Nitrosomonas*

C *Nitrobacter*

D *Pseudomonas*

17. A flask was set up to demonstrate the activity of some of the micro-organisms involved in the nitrogen cycle. The concentration of nitrite in the solution was measured over several weeks and the results are shown in the graph.

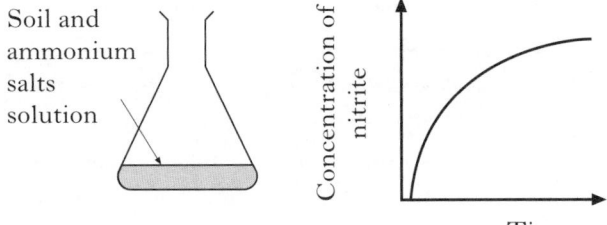

Which process has been shown to be taking place in the flask?

A Ammonification

B Nitrification

C Nitrogen fixation

D Denitrification

18. The graph shows the effect of adding different amounts of fertiliser on the yield of a crop plant.

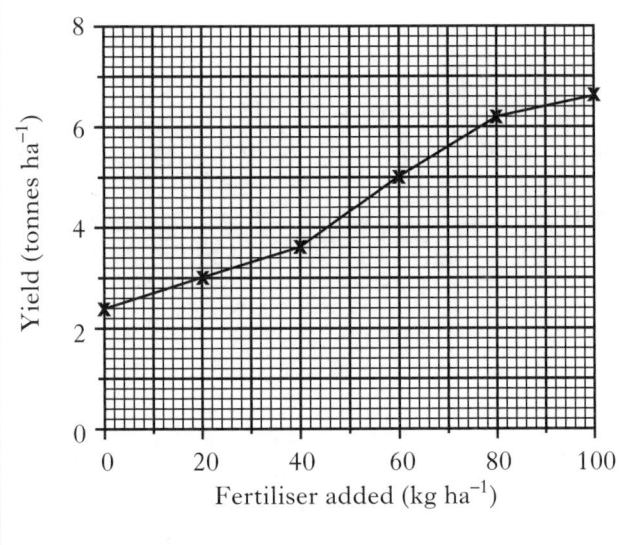

The percentage increase in yield obtained when the fertiliser is increased from 40 to $80 \, kg \, ha^{-1}$ is

A 26

B 40

C 58

D 72.

[Turn over

19. Which of the following is an example of *exploitation* competition?

    A   Red grouse, through aggressive behaviour, establish a territory which provides food and cover.

    B   A population of moose living on an island share a limited supply of food.

    C   Dandelions have evolved a flat rosette leaf arrangement which maximises their supply of light.

    D   Encrusting sponges use poisonous chemicals to overcome other sponge species as they expand to fill open space on rock surfaces.

20. Which of the graphs best represents the relationship between the intensity of rabbit grazing and the diversity of plant species in a series of grassland plots?

21. The piping plover (*Charadrius melodus*) often nests within colonies of the common tern (*Sterna hirundo*). The breeding success of the plover is greater when nesting takes place within a tern colony. The breeding success of terns is very similar in colonies with and without plovers. This suggests that the relationship between the two species is

    A   commensalism

    B   mutualism

    C   parasitism

    D   competitive.

22. The table shows some of the characteristics of a number of agricultural fertilisers.

| | Fertiliser | | | |
Characteristic	A	B	C	D
Phosphate concentration	high	high	low	high
Nitrate concentration	high	low	high	high
Nutrient release rate	slow	slow	fast	fast

Which of these fertilisers would be most likely to cause eutrophication in an aquatic ecosystem?

23. Soils are mixtures of rock particles of different sizes called clay, silt and sand. The table shows the composition of a number of different soil types.

| | Particle size (%) | | |
Soil type	Clay	Silt	Sand
sandy clay loam	20 – 30	0 – 30	50 – 80
clay loam	20 – 35	20 – 60	20 – 50
sandy silt loam	0 – 20	40 – 80	20 – 50
silty clay loam	20 – 35	45 – 80	0 – 20

Which of the following represents a clay loam?

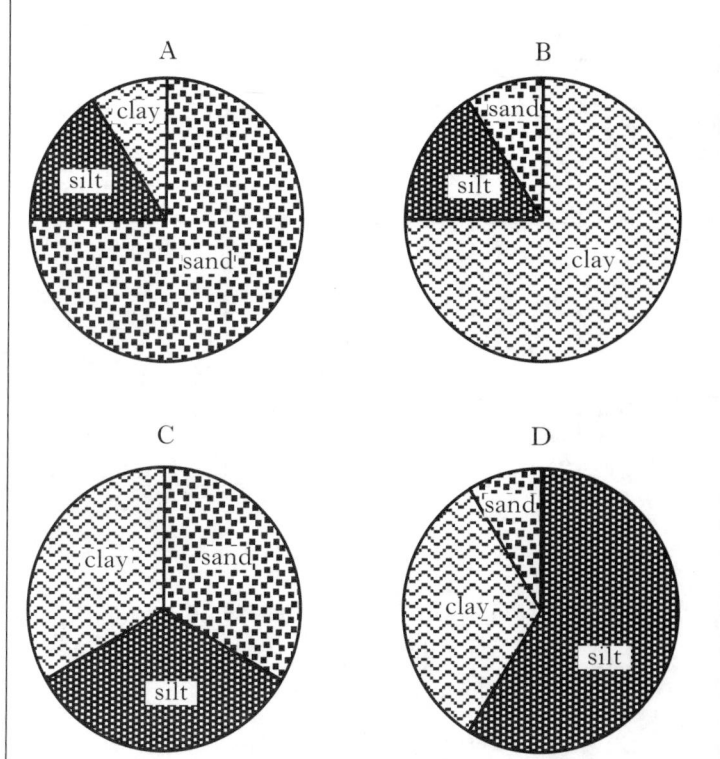

24. The following gases can all be atmospheric pollutants.

1   Carbon dioxide

2   Methane

3   Nitrous oxide

4   Sulphur dioxide

Those that contribute to the formation of acid rain are

A   1, 2, 3 and 4

B   1, 3 and 4 only

C   1, 2 and 4 only

D   3 and 4 only.

25. The figure shows the concentration of dieldrin (a pesticide) in an alga, the water flea *Daphnia* and a small fish known as a guppy. The species were immersed separately in a solution of dieldrin. The *Daphnia* were not fed during the test; the fish were fed on uncontaminated *Daphnia*.

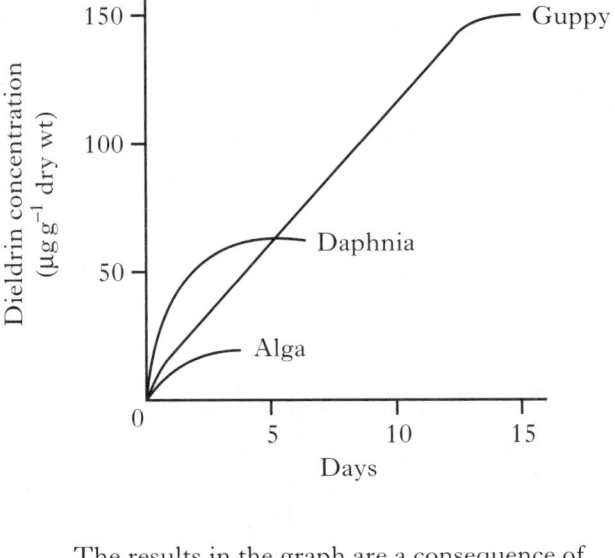

The results in the graph are a consequence of

A   biological magnification

B   bioaccumulation

C   biotransformation

D   biodegradation.

[END OF SECTION A]

Candidates are reminded that the answer sheet MUST be returned INSIDE the front cover of the answer book.

[Turn over for Section B on *Page eight*

SECTION B

All questions in this section should be attempted.
All answers must be written clearly and legibly in ink.

1. The Asian musk shrew (*Suncus murinus*), an efficient and rapid coloniser originating in India, has reached the island of Mauritius. The shrew is frequently transported unknowingly in ships' cargoes and personal baggage. It is responsible for a number of damaging ecological effects and is fast becoming a pest species of global proportions, especially in small island ecosystems.

Figure 1: The Asian musk shrew (*Suncus murinus*)

One conservation programme to eradicate the shrew has been attempted on Ile aux Aigrettes, a small island nature reserve off the coast of Mauritius. In the programme, "live" traps were used with a trap-door mechanism closing behind any animal entering. Traps were checked daily and any shrews caught were killed; other species were released unharmed.

The locations for traps were marked out on a grid to give 1650 potential trapping points covering the whole island. Trapping started in August 1999 at the western end of the island. At intervals of 6 to 15 days, traps were moved progressively across the island until all points had been covered. Five more trapping "sweeps" were carried out to give six in total. Trapping results are shown in Table 1; these are reported as *trap nights*, values obtained by multiplying the number of traps used by the number of nights the sweeps lasted.

The shrew's breeding period lasts from November to March. Pregnant females were only found in traps from late November to January.

Each location was classified according to the four main vegetation types found on the island. The percentage cover of vegetation types is shown in Table 2. Observed and expected capture data in these four vegetation types are shown in Figure 2.

Table 1: Capture rates of shrews during each trapping sweep

Sweep number	Dates (1999–2000)	Number of trap nights	Capture rate (Number of shrews per 10 000 trap nights)
1	Early August	12 804	589
2	Late August	16 569	15
3	Early September	10 080	2
4	Late September	9 669	2
5	October–November	22 751	11
6	December–January	24 740	15

Question 1 (continued)

Table 2: Vegetation types on Ile aux Aigrettes

Vegetation type	Description	Cover (%)
Coastal	Native, dense scrub. No forest	31
Ebony forest	Native tree species	37
"Weeded" forest	Invasive plants removed with native species being replanted	25
Leucaena forest	Monoculture of an introduced species	7

Figure 2: Observed and expected captures in each vegetation type
The expected capture values assume that shrews are uniformly spread across the island and are not affected by vegetation type.

Total number in this capture sample is 524.

[Question 1 continues on *Page ten*

Marks

Question 1 (continued)

(a) (i) What term is used to describe foreign, introduced species such as the Asian musk shrew?   **1**

   (ii) State **one** possible "damaging ecological effect" of such a species.   **1**

(b) Refer to the data in Table 1.

   (i) Explain why capture rates are presented as "number of shrews per 10 000 trap nights".   **1**

   (ii) Initially the conservation team believed the eradication programme was successful. However, by the end, they had to conclude that it had failed.

      Use the data to show why they changed their minds.   **2**

(c) The conservation team concluded that it was important to trap when the shrews were not breeding. How is this conclusion justified by the information given?   **1**

(d) Refer to the data in Table 2 and Figure 2.

   (i) The expected capture values are based on the assumption that the shrews are spread uniformly across the island.

      Using ebony forest as an example, show how the expected capture values were calculated.   **2**

   (ii) In which vegetation type is shrew density at its highest?   **1**

   (iii) What evidence is there that human activity affects shrew distribution?   **1**

(e) Pesticides were considered as a means of eradicating the shrews.

   Describe **one** feature of an ecologically "desirable" pesticide.   **1**

(f) The term "commensal" has been used by the conservation team to describe the shrew's relationship with humans. What is meant by the term commensal?   **1**

(g) Suggest a control measure that could be introduced, in addition to the eradication programme, to help eliminate the Asian musk shrew.   **1**

(13)

[Questions 2, 3 and 4 are on fold-out *Page eleven*

Marks

2. In an investigation into decomposition, discs of oak leaves were enclosed in nylon mesh bags with either large (7 mm) or small (1 mm) mesh size. The bags were then buried in garden soil. The 1 mm mesh excluded larger soil invertebrates such as earthworms and millipedes. The leaf discs were weighed at the start and thereafter at yearly intervals.

Mesh size (mm)	Percentage of leaf disc mass remaining		
	November 2004	November 2005	November 2006
1	100	38	30
7	100	15	8

(a) What term is used to describe invertebrates that feed on dead organic material?   1

(b) Explain why the leaf disc mass decreased faster in 7 mm bags than in 1 mm bags.   2

(c) State **one** final product of the processes taking place inside the nylon bags.   1

(d) A predictable sequence of changes in community structure occurs in the bags as the organic material disappears. What term is used to describe this sequence?   1

(5)

3. Discuss the responses of regulators to variations in the external environment.   **(5)**

4. The liver fluke *Fasciola hepatica* is a parasitic flatworm. The figure shows the relationship between the mean daily egg output per adult worm and the mean number of worms present in its sheep host.

(a) Explain how the decreasing rate of egg production shows a density-dependent effect.   1

(b) The flatworm uses a snail species as a secondary host.

   Describe the role of the snail in the life cycle of the liver fluke.   1

(c) Explain how the health of a sheep may affect the outcome of a fluke infestation.   1

(d) Describe **one** measure that can be used to prevent infestation of a host by a parasite.   1

(4)

Marks

5. *Retinoblastoma* is a rare cancer that develops in the eyes of children. Mutation in both copies of the retinoblastoma (*Rb*) gene results in proliferation of cells that would normally form retinal tissue. The protein arising from the *Rb* gene is abundant in the nucleus of all normal mammalian cells where it has an important role in the cell cycle.

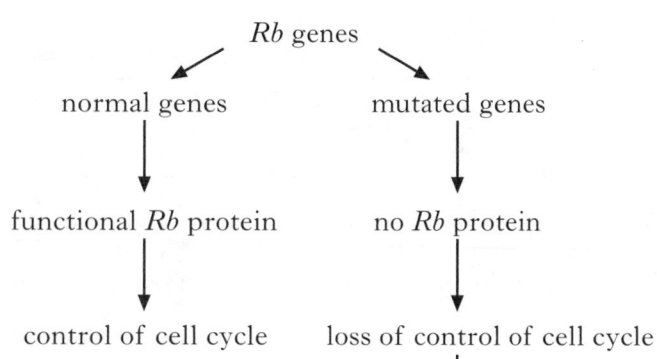

When phosphorylated, the *Rb* protein binds to gene regulatory proteins and prevents them from activating cell proliferation. When unphosphorylated, it cannot bind to the gene regulatory proteins.

(a) Explain why kinase enzyme activity might restrict cell division when functional *Rb* protein is abundant.　　**2**

(b) Explain how the information provided indicates that the *Rb* gene is **not** a proto-oncogene.　　**1**

(3)

6. *Amoeba* is a unicellular organism found in fresh water. It uses a contractile vacuole to eliminate water entering by osmosis. The data below show the concentrations of sodium ions (Na^+) and potassium ions (K^+) in the external medium, cytoplasm and contractile vacuole of *Amoeba* in culture.

	Ion concentrations (mmol L^{-1})		
Ion	*External Medium*	*Cytoplasm*	*Vacuole*
sodium	0·2	0·6	19·8
potassium	0·1	31·0	4·6

Amoeba (labelled: nucleus, cytoplasm, vesicle, contractile vacuole)

(a) Give **two** characteristics that would distinguish prokaryotic organisms from an *Amoeba*.　　**1**

(b) Show as a whole number ratio the relative concentrations of sodium ions in the external medium, cytoplasm and vacuole.　　**1**

(c) It is thought that the contractile vacuole is formed from smaller vesicles containing fluid isotonic with the cytoplasm. Ion concentrations are then changed as a result of ion pump activity.

Explain how the data could support the hypothesis that a sodium-potassium pump may be working across the vacuole membrane but not across the plasma membrane.　　**3**

(5)

Marks

7. Figure 1 below shows the two alleles, *B1* and *B2*, for a gene. Within *B1* there are sites where a restriction enzyme can cut; in *B2*, the allele has a mutation at one of the restriction sites, which prevents a cut.

A probe complementary to a short portion of the DNA can bind at the position shown in Figure 1.

Figure 1

Samples of DNA from a family of two parents and their four children were digested with the same restriction enzyme. The fragments were separated by electrophoresis and tested with the probe. The results for family members are identified with the numbers 1 to 6, as shown in Figure 2.

Figure 2

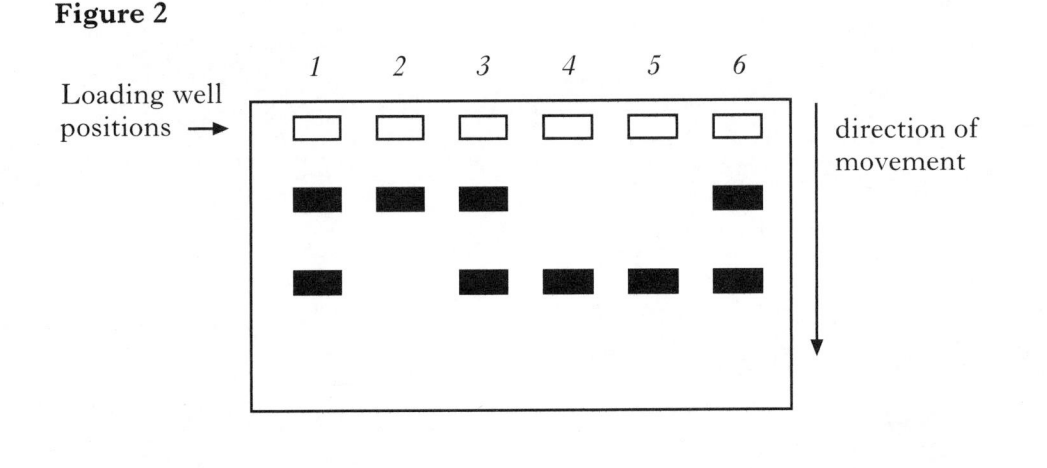

(*a*) Why is DNA able to move in the electrophoresis gel? **1**

(*b*) Explain how the results show that individuals 1, 3 and 6 have the genotype *B1B2*. **2**

(*c*) What is the genotype of individual 2? **1**

(*d*) Identify **two** individuals who could be the parents in this family. **1**

(5)

[Turn over

Marks

8. Answer **either** A **or** B.

    A. Describe the growth of cells under the following headings:

        (i)   control mechanisms of the cell cycle;   **6**

        (ii) culturing of mammalian cells.   **9**

  OR   **(15)**

    B. Give an account of cell membranes under the following headings:

        (i)   the structure of phospholipids;   **6**

        (ii)   the composition of the plasma membrane;   **3**

        (iii) functions of membrane proteins.   **6**

        (15)

[END OF SECTION B]

SECTION C

Candidates should attempt questions on <u>one unit</u>, <u>either</u> Biotechnology <u>or</u> Animal Behaviour <u>or</u> Physiology, Health and Exercise.

The questions on Animal Behaviour can be found on pages 18–21.

The questions on Physiology, Health and Exercise can be found on pages 22–24.

All answers must be written clearly and legibly in ink.

Labelled diagrams may be used where appropriate.

Marks

Biotechnology

1. The diagram shows a fermenter used to grow large numbers of micro-organisms for enzyme production. To achieve rapid growth, particular conditions are needed.

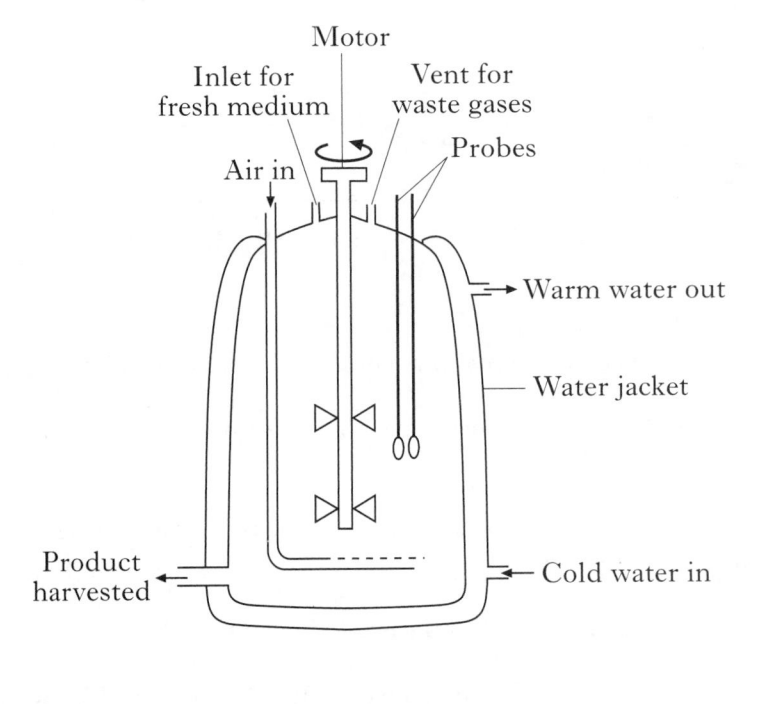

(a) Give **one** precaution that needs to be taken to prevent contamination by other micro-organisms during enzyme production.

1

(b) Explain the purpose of the water jacket in this fermenter.

1

(c) Name an enzyme produced commercially from:

   (i) a naturally occurring micro-organism;

   (ii) a genetically modified micro-organism.

2

(4)

2. Antibiotics are produced commercially in large-scale industrial fermenters.

Give an account of how a pure antibiotic product could be recovered at the end of the fermentation.

(5)

[Turn over

Biotechnology **(continued)**   *Marks*

3. An investigation was carried out to determine how different energy sources affect the growth of *E. coli*. The figure shows viable counts of cells grown in three separate fermenters (A, B and C); each fermenter had a different energy source.

(a) What is the difference between a total count and a viable count?   1

(b) Use data from the figure to describe how the growth of *E. coli* in 1% glucose is different from that in 1% lactose.   2

(c) (i) The following equation is used to calculate the growth rate constant, k, of a bacterial population.

$$k = \frac{\ln 2}{g}, \text{ where } ln2 = 0\cdot693 \text{ and } g \text{ is the time in hours for the population to double.}$$

Calculate the growth rate constant for fermenter B between 80 and 100 minutes.   1

(ii) How could calculation of growth rate constants be used to determine when culture conditions are no longer optimal?   1

(d) The diauxic growth demonstrated by *E. coli* in fermenter A is dependent on the synthesis of β-galactosidase. Briefly describe the role of CAP in stimulating the synthesis of this enzyme.   2

                                                                                          (7)

Biotechnology **(continued)**   *Marks*

4. Genetic manipulation of bacteria can be achieved by the introduction of plasmids containing DNA sequences from other organisms. The diagram shows a plasmid containing resistance genes for the antibiotics ampicillin and tetracycline, before and after the insertion of a DNA sequence.

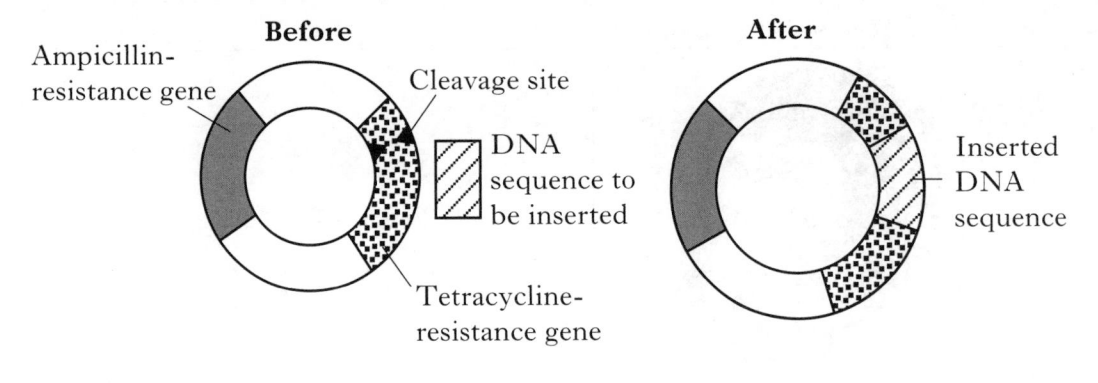

There are two possible problems with this approach:

   (i)   only some of the plasmids take up the DNA sequence;

   (ii) only a small percentage of bacterial cells take up a plasmid of any kind.

Bacteria containing plasmids with the desirable DNA sequence can be selected by culturing them on media containing antibiotics. The same colonies are plated in the same grid positions on the two plates shown below.

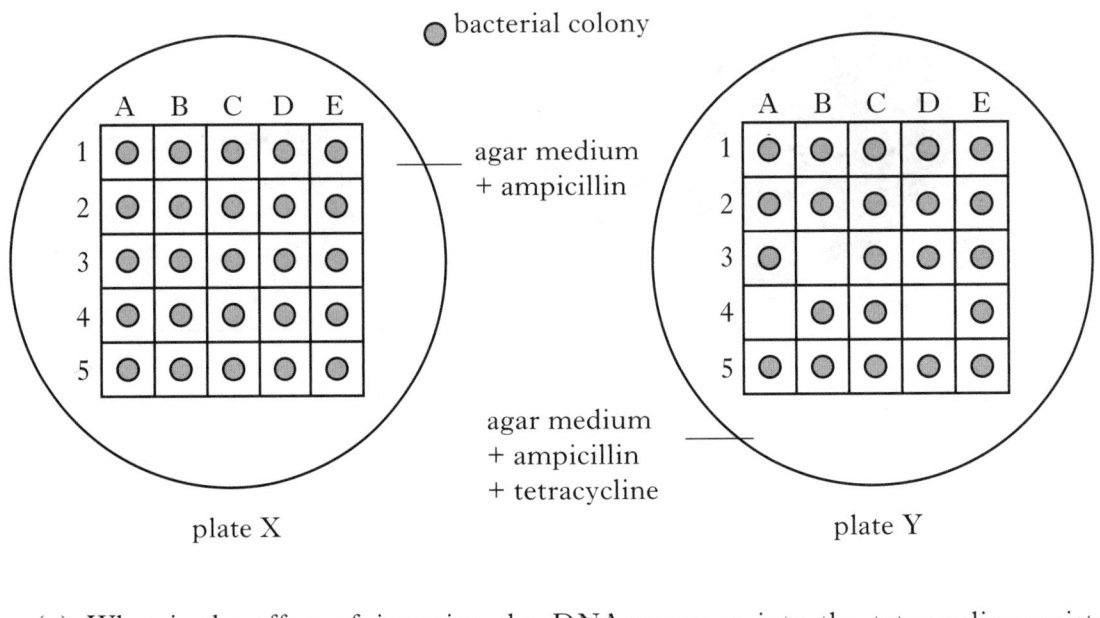

(a) What is the effect of inserting the DNA sequence into the tetracycline-resistance gene?   1

(b) Explain why the colonies A4, B3 and D4 from plate Y would be selected for further analysis.   2

(c) Give an example of an agricultural use of this technique.   1

                                                                              (4)

                                                                              (20)

[End of *Biotechnology* questions. *Animal Behaviour* questions start on Page 18]

SECTION C (continued)   *Marks*

Animal Behaviour

1. Chimpanzees (*Pan troglodytes*) are social primates. The table shows a list of facial expressions that are used in group interactions.

Facial expression		Interaction
Pout		Begging for food
Full open grin		Displaying fear or excitement
Fear grin		Approaching a higher-ranking chimpanzee

   (*a*) What term is used to describe a list of this type?   **1**

   (*b*) Using an example from the table, explain the meaning of the term *anthropomorphism*.   **1**

   (*c*) Other than the use of facial expressions, name a behaviour in primates that is used to strengthen social bonds between the individuals in a group.   **1**

   (3)

Animal Behaviour **(continued)**   *Marks*

2. Some males of the cichlid species *Astatotilapia burtoni* are territorial and vigorously defend their territory by fighting. Territorial males have brightly coloured bodies, a black eyebar and orange spots on their anal fin. Non-territorial males and females lack any of these bright or contrasting colours or patterns. The eggs of the females are very similar in appearance to the orange spots on the anal fins of territorial males.

black eyebar ———   ——— orange spots

Figures 1 and 2 below show the rate of attack response of territorial males to two different dummy fish.

Figure 1
Dummy: eyebar present; orange spots absent

Figure 2
Dummy: eyebar absent; orange spots present

(a) Using data from Figures 1 and 2, compare the responses to the two dummies in relation to frequency of attacks.   2

(b) Suggest an explanation for the response shown in Figure 2.   1

(c) What benefit do successful males gain through fighting?   1

(d) To what extent does *A. burtoni* show sexual dimorphism?   1

[Turn over

Animal Behaviour **Question 2 (continued)**   *Marks*

(e)   The table below summarises data from experiments investigating the development of the attack response of *A. burtoni*.

Rearing conditions	Stimuli provoking attack response
Reared alone	Black eyebar model Male of own species
Reared by own species	Black eyebar model Male of own species
Reared by foster species	Black eyebar model Male of own species Male of foster species

What two pieces of evidence indicate that the development of attack response behaviour in *A. burtoni* depends on the interaction between genetic and environmental influences?   **2**

(7)

3.   The cuckoo (*Cuculus canorus*) is a *brood parasite* of some species of small birds that nest in Scotland.

(a)   What is the ultimate cause of nest-building behaviour in birds?   **1**

(b)   The female cuckoo lays an egg in the host nest. Typical eggs of hosts and cuckoos are shown below.

Host species   *Host species egg   Cuckoo egg*

Species 1

Species 2

Species 3

What term could be used to describe the close match in appearance between the cuckoo eggs and the host species' eggs?   **1**

Animal Behaviour **Question 3 (continued)**   *Marks*

    (*c*)   The figure shows the feeding behaviour of a young cuckoo.

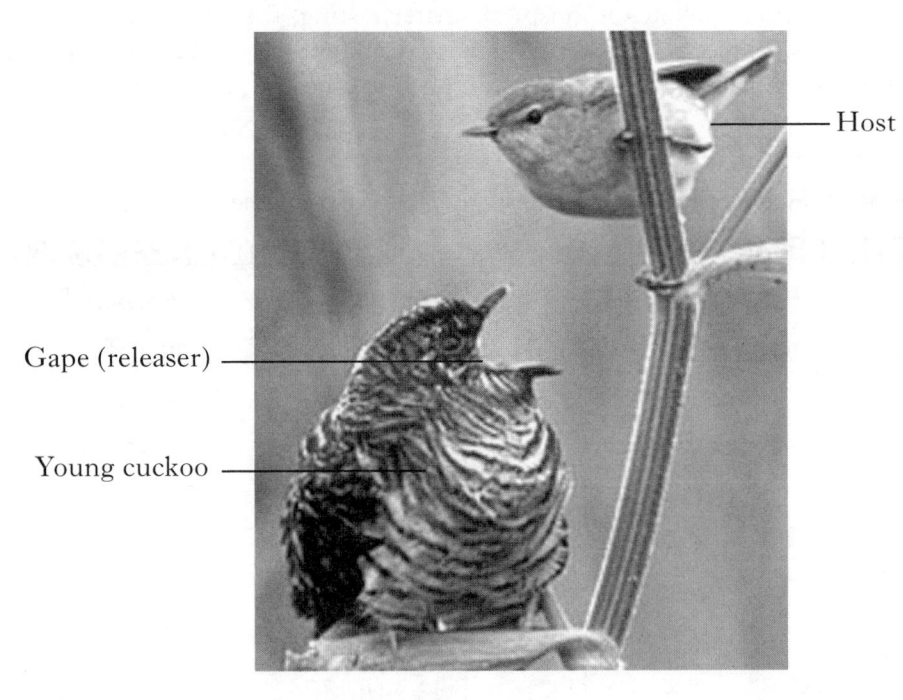

        The hatchling cuckoo bears little resemblance to the host's hatchlings.

        What compels the host to feed the young cuckoo?   **1**

    (*d*)   Explain why the relationship between the host and the cuckoo is **not** an example of
        reciprocal altruism.   **2**

                                                                         (5)

4.   Imprinting is a feature of bird behaviour.

     Discuss the process of imprinting.   **(5)**

                                                                          (20)

**[End of *Animal Behaviour* questions. *Physiology, Health and Exercise* questions
start on Page 22]**

                                                                          [Turn over

SECTION C (continued)   *Marks*

Physiology, Health and Exercise

1. Two patients were tested for diabetes in hospital. After fasting, their blood glucose was measured at 09:00 hours. They were given a glucose drink and their blood glucose was monitored over the following 3 hours (Glucose Tolerance Test). The test results are shown below.

City General Hospital		City General Hospital	
OUTPATIENTS DEPARTMENT		**OUTPATIENTS DEPARTMENT**	
Name	Patient A	Name	Patient B
Glucose Tolerance Test		Glucose Tolerance Test	
	Blood Glucose Concentration		Blood Glucose Concentration
Time	(mmol/L)	Time	(mmol/L)
09:00	4·4	09:00	7·8
09:30	6·8	09:30	11·7
10:00	6·1	10:00	13·9
10:30	5·4	10:30	15·0
11:00	5·3	11:00	16·1
11:30	4·9	11:30	15·5
12:00	4·5	12:00	15·5

(a) Give **two** pieces of evidence from the test results that could be used to identify the diabetic patient.   2

(b) What is the role of glucagon in the control of blood glucose concentration?   1

(c) (i) State the major risk factor in the onset of non insulin-dependent diabetes mellitus (NIDDM).   1

   (ii) Give **two** ways by which regular exercise can help in the control of NIDDM.   2

   (6)

Physiology, Health and Exercise **(continued)** *Marks*

2. Basal metabolic rate (BMR) can be calculated using the following equations:

Males	
Age 10–17 years:	BMR(MJ/day) = 0·074 × body mass (kg) + 2·754
Age 18–29 years:	BMR(MJ/day) = 0·063 × body mass (kg) + 2·896
Females	
Age 10–17 years:	BMR(MJ/day) = 0·056 × body mass (kg) + 2·898
Age 18–29 years:	BMR(MJ/day) = 0·062 × body mass (kg) + 2·036

   (a) Calculate the basal metabolic rate for a 26 year old woman with a mass of 75 kg. **1**

   (b) Energy expenditure can be determined by measuring the oxygen uptake from breathed air. Explain why this procedure is referred to as indirect calorimetry. **1**

   (c) Explain how different factors affect BMR. **5**

   (7)

3. The table shows data from maximal testing of an individual, before and after a period of endurance training. The data can be used to calculate $VO_{2\,max}$.

Measurement	Before training	After training
Left ventricular mass (g)	210	300
Maximum stroke volume (ml)	120	180
Maximum heart rate (beats/min)	175	195
Maximum oxygen uptake (L/min)	3·1	4·6
Body mass (kg)	60	60

   (a) Which measurements from the table would be used to calculate:

   (i) $VO_{2\,max}$ **1**

   (ii) cardiac output? **1**

   (b) What evidence from the table indicates that this individual has developed cardiac hypertrophy? **1**

   (c) Describe how $VO_{2\,max}$ is determined using sub-maximal testing. **1**

   (4)

   [Turn over for Question 4 on *Page twenty four*

Physiology, Health and Exercise **(continued)**   *Marks*

4.   The force exerted by the blood against the walls of blood vessels is known as blood pressure. The figure shows changes in arterial blood pressure of a 20 year old female and a 45 year old male.

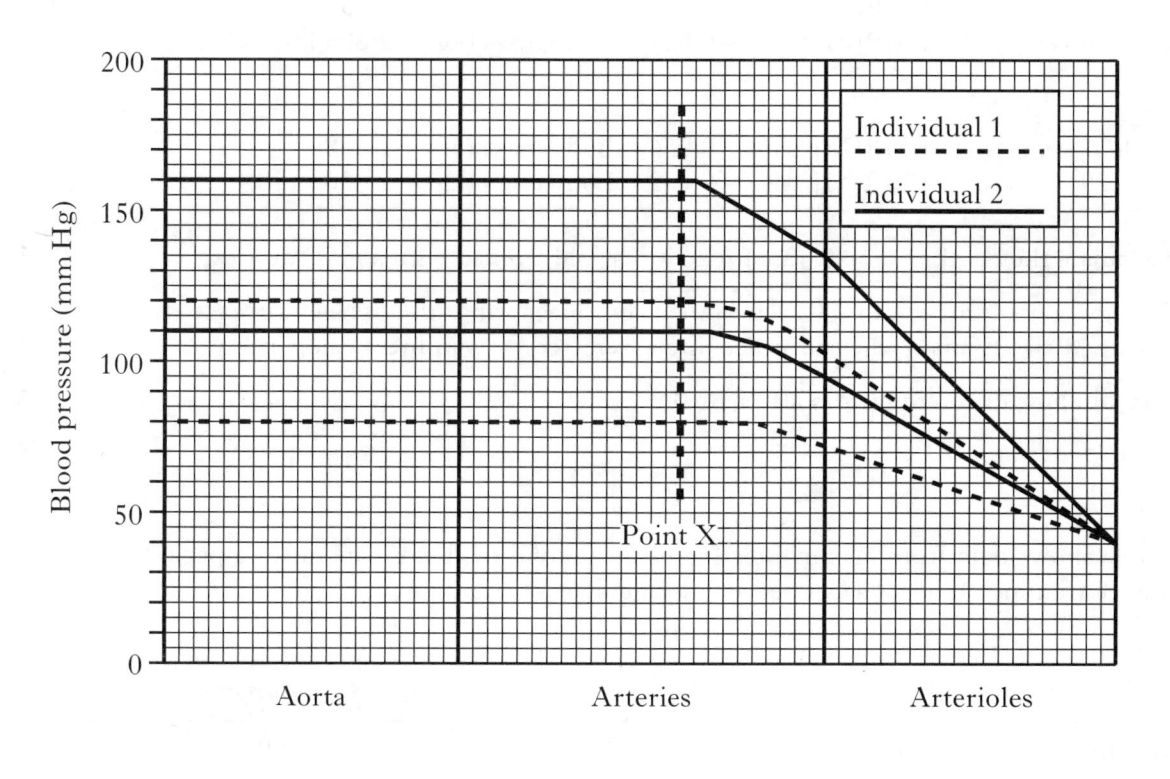

A medical examination showed that the 45 year old had hypertension.

(a)   State **two** modifiable conditions that can influence the development of hypertension.   **2**

(b)   What is the diastolic blood pressure of the 45 year old man at point X on the graph?   **1**

(3)

(20)

[END OF QUESTION PAPER]

[BLANK PAGE]

X007/701

NATIONAL QUALIFICATIONS 2008	TUESDAY, 27 MAY 1.00 PM – 3.30 PM	BIOLOGY ADVANCED HIGHER

SECTION A–Questions 1—25 (25 marks)

Instructions for completion of Section A are given on *Page two*.

SECTIONS B AND C

The answer to each question should be written in ink in the answer book provided. Any additional paper (if used) should be placed inside the front cover of the answer book.

Rough work should be scored through.

Section B (55 marks)

All questions should be attempted. Candidates should note that Question 8 contains a choice.

Question 1 is on Pages 10, 11 and 12. Questions 2, 3 and 4 are on Page 13. Pages 12 and 13 are fold-out pages.

Section C (20 marks)

Candidates should attempt the questions in **one** unit, **either** Biotechnology **or** Animal Behaviour **or** Physiology, Health and Exercise.

Read carefully

1   Check that the answer sheet provided is for **Biology Advanced Higher (Section A)**.

2   For this section of the examination you must use an **HB pencil** and, where necessary, an eraser.

3   Check that the answer sheet you have been given has **your name**, **date of birth**, **SCN** (Scottish Candidate Number) and **Centre Name** printed on it.

Do not change any of these details.

4   If any of this information is wrong, tell the Invigilator immediately.

5   If this information is correct, **print** your name and seat number in the boxes provided.

6   The answer to each question is **either** A, B, C or D. Decide what your answer is, then, using your pencil, put a horizontal line in the space provided (see sample question below).

7   There is **only one correct** answer to each question.

8   Any rough working should be done on the question paper or the rough working sheet, **not** on your answer sheet.

9   At the end of the exam, put the **answer sheet for Section A inside the front cover of the answer book**.

Sample Question

Which of the following molecules contains six carbon atoms?

A   Glucose

B   Pyruvic acid

C   Ribulose bisphosphate

D   Acetyl coenzyme A

The correct answer is **A**—Glucose. The answer **A** has been clearly marked in **pencil** with a horizontal line (see below).

Changing an answer

If you decide to change your answer, carefully erase your first answer and using your pencil, fill in the answer you want. The answer below has been changed to **D**.

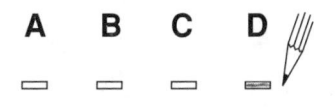

SECTION A

All questions in this section should be attempted.

Answers should be given on the separate answer sheet provided.

1. Which of the following genes encode proteins that promote normal cell division?

   A   Oncogenes

   B   Regulatory genes

   C   Proliferation genes

   D   Anti-proliferation genes

2. The cell cycle is believed to be monitored at checkpoints where specific conditions must be met for the cycle to continue.

   Condition 1:   chromosome alignment

   Condition 2:   successful DNA replication

   Condition 3:   cell size

   Which line in the table correctly shows the condition fulfilled at each checkpoint?

	G1	G2	M
A	2	3	1
B	3	1	2
C	2	1	3
D	3	2	1

3. Which line in the table correctly describes the chemical reaction that breaks down a disaccharide into its monomer subunits?

	Type of reaction	Type of bond broken
A	hydrolysis	peptide
B	condensation	glycosidic
C	hydrolysis	glycosidic
D	condensation	peptide

4. An unbranched polysaccharide is made up of glucose monomers joined together by $\beta(1\rightarrow4)$ linkages. The polysaccharide described could be

   A   amylose

   B   amylopectin

   C   glycogen

   D   cellulose.

5. Which of the following is a covalent bond that stabilises the tertiary structure of a protein?

   A   Hydrogen bond

   B   Disulphide bond

   C   Glycosidic bond

   D   Ester linkage

6. In the diagrams below, the sugar-phosphate backbone of a DNA strand is represented by a vertical line showing 5' to 3' polarity. The horizontal lines between bases represent hydrogen bonds.

   Which diagram represents correctly a short stretch of a DNA molecule?

7. If ten percent of the bases in a molecule of DNA are adenine, what is the ratio of adenine to guanine in the same molecule?

   A   1:1

   B   1:2

   C   1:3

   D   1:4

[Turn over

8. Which line in the table below correctly summarises the movement of sodium and potassium ions into and out of a cell by a sodium-potassium pump?

	Potassium ions	Sodium ions
A	in	out
B	in	in
C	out	in
D	out	out

9. Which of the following is a component of the cytoskeleton?

A Phospholipid

B Tubulin

C Peptidoglycan

D Glycoprotein

10. A length of DNA is cut into fragments by the restriction enzymes BamHI and EcoRI

▼ BamHI cut site

△ EcoRI cut site

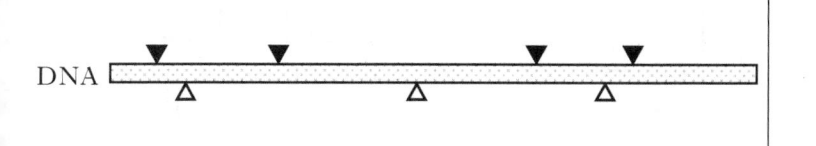

DNA

Which line in the table below correctly identifies the number of DNA fragments obtained?

	DNA cut by BamH1 only	DNA cut by EcoR1 only	DNA cut by both BamH1 and EcoR1
A	5	4	8
B	4	5	8
C	5	4	9
D	4	5	9

11. The diagram below outlines the stages involved in the polymerase chain reaction.

Which line in the table correctly identifies temperature X and the structures labelled Y?

	Temperature X (°C)	Structure Y
A	55	probe
B	95	primer
C	55	primer
D	95	probe

12. The result of profiling various DNA samples in a criminal investigation is shown below.

Key:
1 blood sample of victim
2 blood sample of suspect X
3 blood sample of suspect Y
4 first sample from forensic evidence
5 second sample from forensic evidence

1 2 3 4 5

Which of the following could the DNA analyst conclude about the crime?

A Only suspect X was involved

B Only suspect Y was involved

C Suspects X and Y were both involved

D Neither suspect X nor Y was involved

13. Which of the following micro-organisms is responsible for the conversion of nitrite to nitrate in soil?

    A *Nitrobacter*

    B *Pseudomonas*

    C *Nitrosomonas*

    D *Rhizobium*

Questions 14 and 15 relate to the diagram below, which shows the recycling of carbon in the environment.

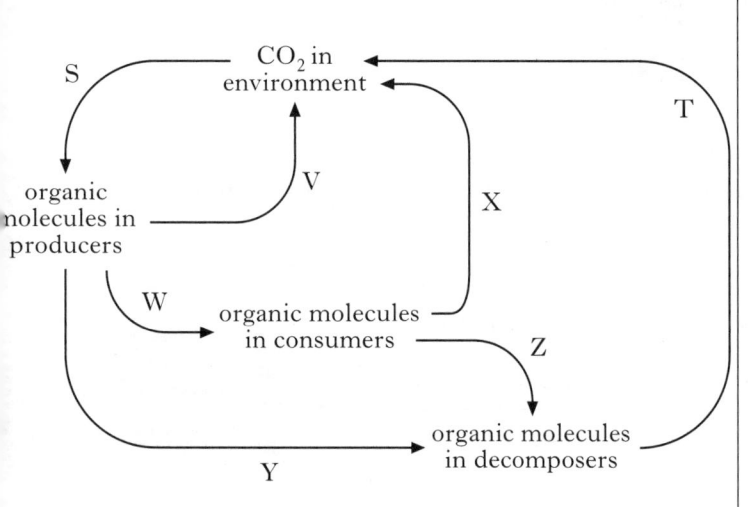

14. Which line in the table below describes correctly the processes that are occurring at stages S, V and W?

	Transformation	Fixation	Respiration
A	W	S	V
B	W	V	S
C	V	S	W
D	S	W	V

15. Coral bleaching could increase if process S is

    A greater than V + X + T

    B greater than W + Y + Z

    C less than W + Y + Z

    D less than V + X + T.

16. Which line in the table matches a group of organisms correctly with their type of nutrition?

	Group of organisms	Type of nutrition
A	producers	heterotrophic
B	consumers	autotrophic
C	decomposers	autotrophic
D	consumers	heterotrophic

17. Population size can be estimated using the following formula:

    $$P = \frac{n_1 \times n_2}{n_3}$$

    where P = population estimate

    n_1 = number first captured, marked and released

    n_2 = total number in second capture

    n_3 = number of marked individuals recaptured.

    In a survey to estimate a woodlouse population, the following data were obtained:

    Woodlice captured, marked and released = 40
    Marked woodlice in second capture   = 12
    Unmarked woodlice in second capture   = 48

    The estimated population of the woodlice was

    A 100

    B 160

    C 200

    D 1920.

18. Which of the following is a density-independent effect?

    A A decrease in temperature increasing the abundance of a tree species.

    B An increase in food supply increasing the abundance of a herbivore.

    C A decrease in predators increasing the abundance of a prey species.

    D An increase in competitors decreasing the yield of a crop species.

[Turn over

19. The figure shows the results of red deer population surveys in two areas of the same size.

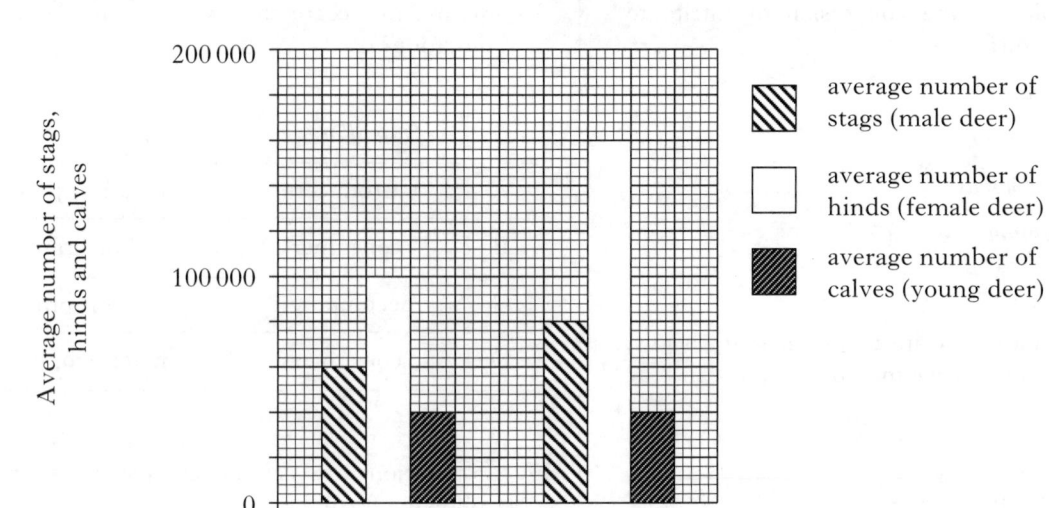

Which line in the table below correctly shows the effect of a change in population density on the birth rate of red deer?

	Population density	Proportion of hinds having calves
A	increases	decreases
B	decreases	decreases
C	increases	increases
D	decreases	stays the same

20. Parasitism is a form of symbiosis. A parasite that is facultative

 A benefits from its host but does not harm it

 B can be associated with a host but can also live independently

 C is passed to its main host from a secondary host

 D has a relationship with its host from which both benefit.

21. The marine iguana (*Amblyrhyncus cristatus*) of the Galapagos Islands basks in the sunshine before swimming for food in the cold sea water. Which line of the table correctly describes the iguana and its temperature regulating mechanism?

	Type of organism	Mechanism
A	homeothermic	behavioural
B	homeothermic	physiological
C	poikilothermic	behavioural
D	poikilothermic	physiological

22. The Puerto Rican lizard *Anolis cristatellus* is found both in shaded forests and in open sunlit areas.

The graph below shows the relationship between air temperature and body temperature of lizards occupying each habitat.

Which line in the table shows the response of the lizards to changes in air temperature in each habitat?

	Open habitat	Shaded forest habitat
A	regulation	regulation
B	regulation	conformation
C	conformation	conformation
D	conformation	regulation

23. Common terns (*Sterna hirundo*) feed on fish and nest colonially on land. Nesting terns often attempt to steal fish from neighbouring terns in their colony.

What term describes correctly this type of competitive interaction?

A   Exploitation competition

B   Interference competition

C   Competitive exclusion

D   Resource partitioning

24. The diagram below shows the distribution of two species of barnacle. The fundamental and realised niches of the two species are shown by the vertical lines W, X, Y and Z. The realised niche of species 2 is line Z.

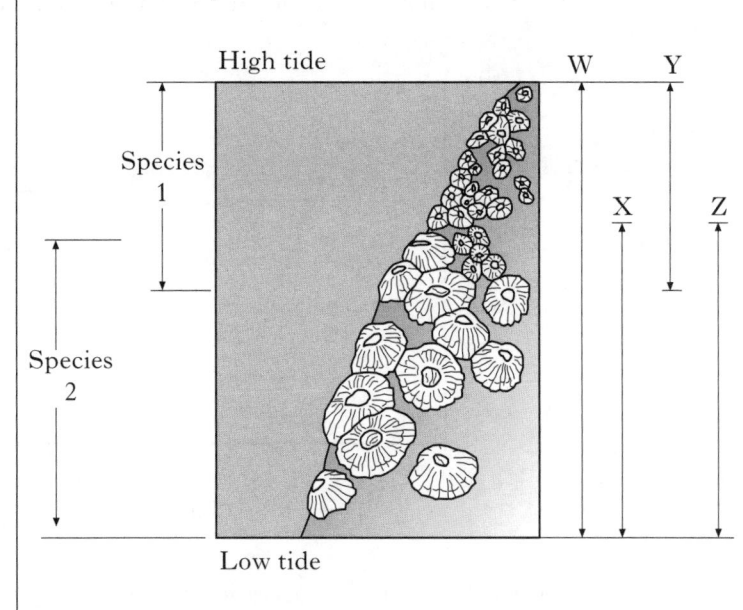

Which line in the table below identifies correctly the other niches?

	Fundamental niche of species 1	Fundamental niche of species 2	Realised niche of species 1
A	W	X	Y
B	Y	X	W
C	W	Y	X
D	X	W	Y

[Turn over

25. Flagellates and ciliates are aerobic, unicellular organisms that feed on bacteria. Commonly referred to as protozoa, they are used in the *activated sludge* process to break down sewage. Different species of ciliates have different lifestyles—free-swimming, crawling and sedentary (attached by a stalk to the surface). There are typically 50 000 ciliates per cm^3 of sludge sample.

The graph shows succession in the development of activated sludge.

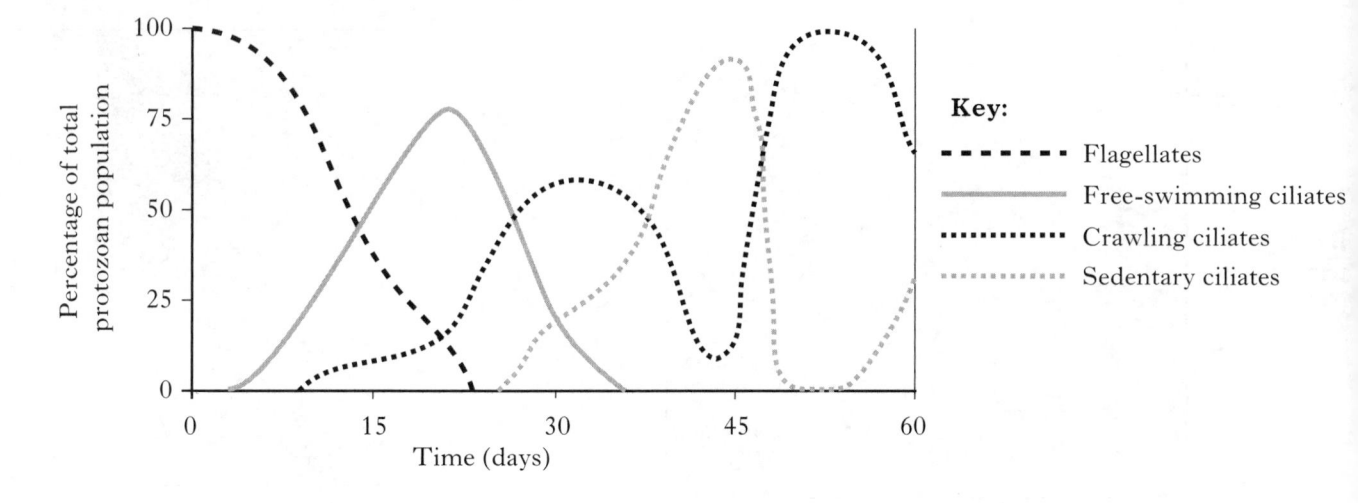

On which day in the succession would a sample contain 30 000 per cm^3 crawling and 10 000 per cm^3 free-swimming ciliates?

A   15

B   20

C   30

D   35

[*END OF SECTION A*]

**Candidates are reminded that the answer sheet MUST be returned INSIDE the
front cover of the answer book.**

[Turn over for Section B on Page ten

SECTION B

All questions in this section should be attempted.
All answers must be written clearly and legibly in ink.

1. In 1992, a membrane protein called *aquaporin-1* (AQP1) was found to function exclusively as a channel for the passage of water molecules. The AQP1 molecule spans the phospholipid bilayer; each of its four linked subunits is a separate water channel (Figure 1).

Figure 1: Aquaporin-1 in a membrane

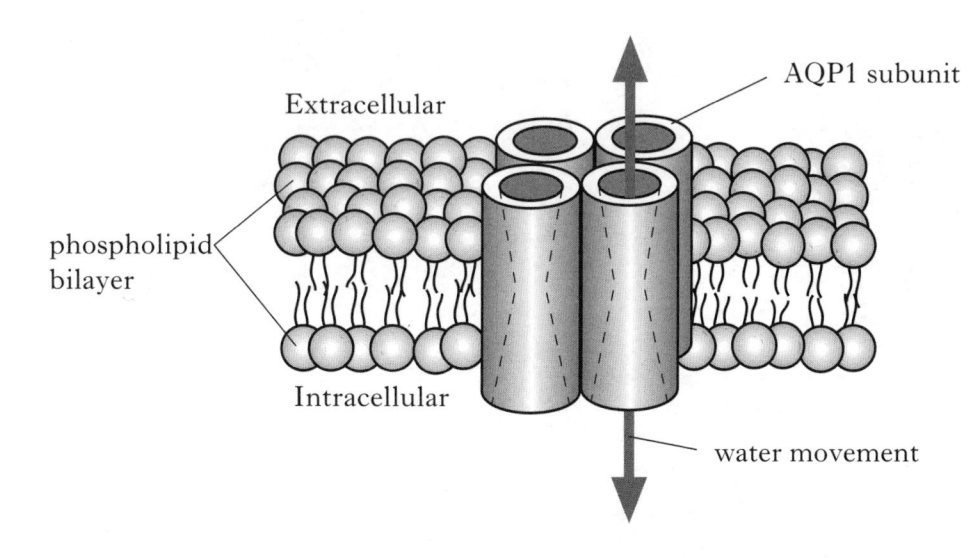

Early experiments were designed to determine the role of these protein channels in water movement. Researchers removed the contents of red blood cells to leave structures consisting of only the plasma membranes; these are known as "red cell ghosts". The ghosts were filled with solutions containing radioactive water and the concentration gradient across the membrane was varied. The rate at which water molecules moved out of the ghosts was measured in isotonic and hypertonic external solutions, before and after a treatment that inactivates AQP1.

From their results, summarised in the Table, the researchers concluded that the very rapid transfer of water across membranes during osmosis was through the AQP1 channels.

Table: Rate of water movement across ghost membranes

	Rate of water movement (units s^{-1})	
External solution	Untreated AQP1	Treated AQP1
Isotonic	2·5	1·0
Hypertonic	20	1·8

Recent studies have shown that several different aquaporins exist and they are present in a number of organs including eyes, brain, lungs and kidneys; all of them are important in water transport across membranes. In kidneys, they are found in some parts of the nephrons (Figure 2) where they have a role in water balance.

Question 1 (continued)

Figure 2:   Nephron

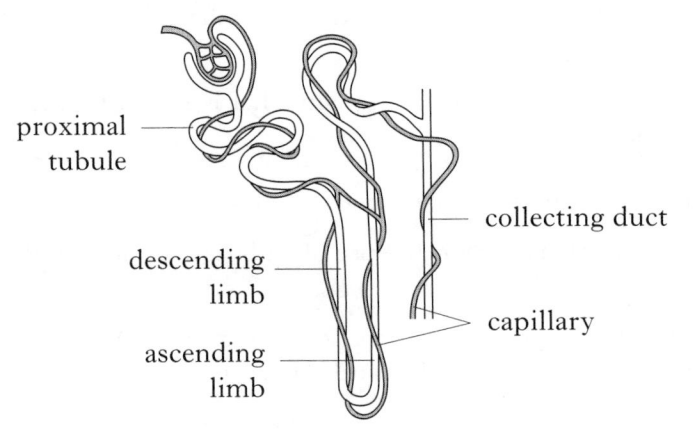

AQP1 is present only in the cells lining the proximal tubule, descending limb and in the capillaries associated with the nephron. About 70% of the water entering the nephron is reabsorbed here. A different aquaporin, AQP2, is present in cells of the collecting duct. The number of AQP2 molecules active at a cell surface increases with the concentration of antidiuretic hormone (ADH) in blood. ADH secretion is increased so that more water is reabsorbed into the capillaries from urine in the duct.

To study the importance of aquaporins in kidney function, three groups of mice with different genotypes were selected.

Group 1: genotype NN: homozygous for the presence of AQP1;

Group 2: genotype Nn: heterozygous;

Group 3: genotype nn: homozygous recessive; AQP1 absent.

Body mass and urine solute concentration were measured before and after a period without water. The results are shown in Figure 3 and Figure 4.

Figure 3: % change in body mass of mice after a period without water

Figure 4: Urine solute concentration before (H) and after (D) a period without water

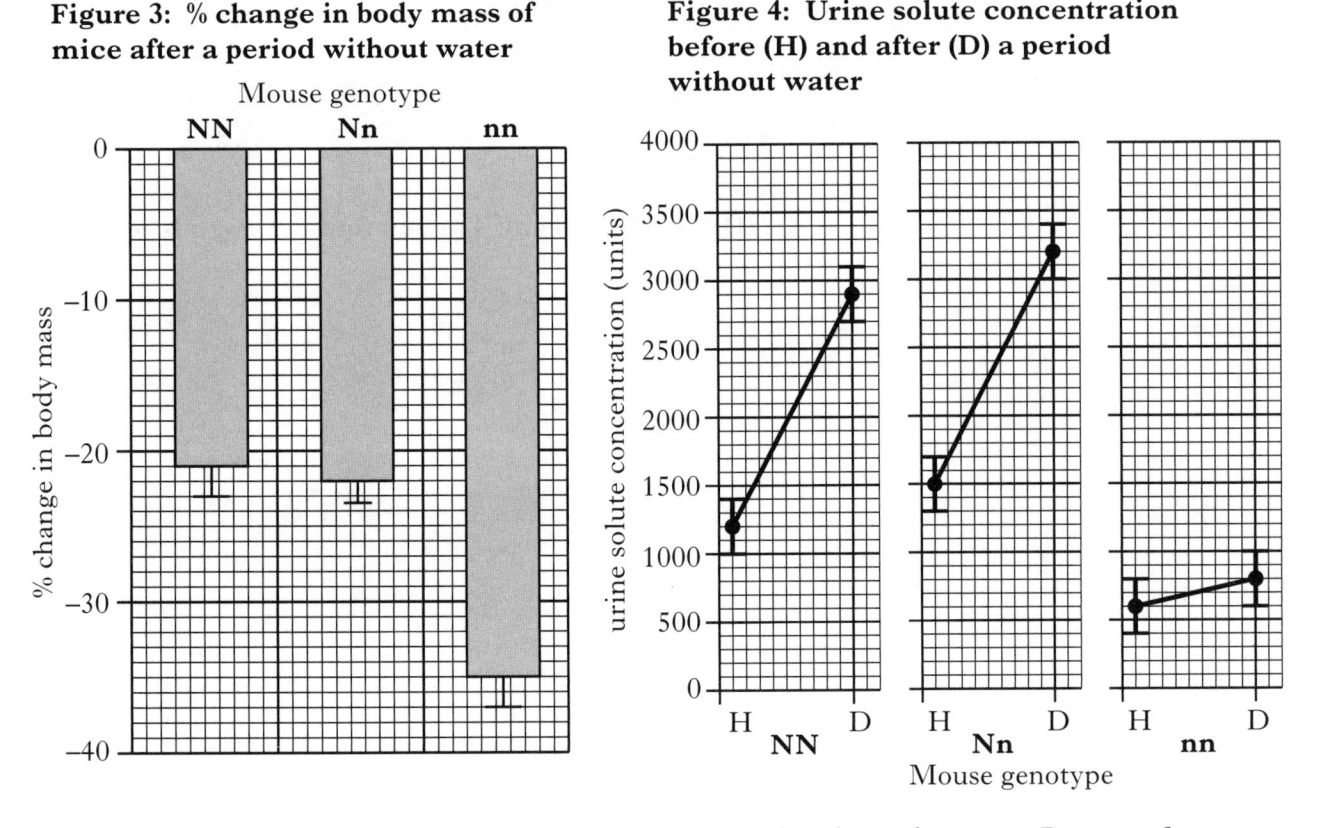

[Question 1 continues on *Page twelve*

Question 1 (continued)

Marks

(a) (i) What term describes a protein that is embedded in a membrane rather than attached to the surface?

1

(ii) With reference to aquaporin, explain what is meant by the quaternary structure of a protein.

1

(b) Refer to the experimental work using red cell ghosts.

(i) Suggest an explanation for the use of radioactive water in the solutions placed in the ghosts.

1

(ii) The Table shows that in isotonic conditions when AQP1 has been treated, water molecules flow out of the ghost cells at a rate of $1 \cdot 0$ units s^{-1}.

Explain why there would be no overall change in cell volume in these conditions.

1

(iii) Aquaporins were inactivated by phosphorylation.

Which type of enzyme adds phosphate to a protein?

1

(iv) Use data from the Table to show that functioning aquaporins can increase water flow across a membrane by over 1000%.

2

(c) (i) Figure 3 shows that homozygous recessive mice lost about 35% of their body mass during the period when they had no water supply.

Explain how these results may lead to the conclusion that the homozygous recessive mice lost abnormally high amounts of water in their urine.

2

(ii) Refer to Figure 3 and Figure 4. Use the data to show that heterozygous mice are producing enough AQP1 molecules for normal osmoregulation.

3

(d) Humans with a condition called *nephrogenic diabetes insipidus* (NDI) have normal AQP1 and ADH production but have non-functioning AQP2.

(i) Predict the effect of a period of dehydration on urine production by individuals with NDI compared to individuals without NDI.

1

(ii) Explain your prediction.

1

(14)

[Questions 2, 3 and 4 are on fold-out *Page thirteen*

Marks

2. (*a*) (i) Identify structure X shown in the diagram below. **1**

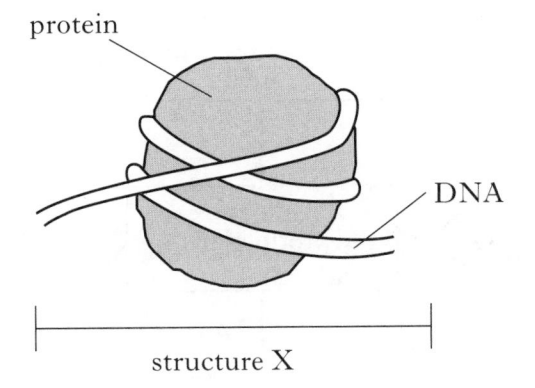

(ii) Why is the binding of DNA to this type of protein so important for eukaryotic cells? **2**

(*b*) In the production of transgenic plants, the genome of a plant species can be modified by incubating protoplasts with engineered plasmids.

    (i) Name the prokaryotic species used as the source of these plasmids. **1**

    (ii) Describe how protoplasts are produced from isolated plant cells. **1**

(5)

3. Describe the general structure of steroids and their function in cell signalling. **(4)**

4. The diagram below represents an enzyme, PRPP synthetase, involved at the start of the biochemical pathway that produces nucleotides. In the active site there are two positions (S) where the substrate molecules, ribose and ATP, bind and react. Position I is an inhibitor binding site and position A is an activator binding site.

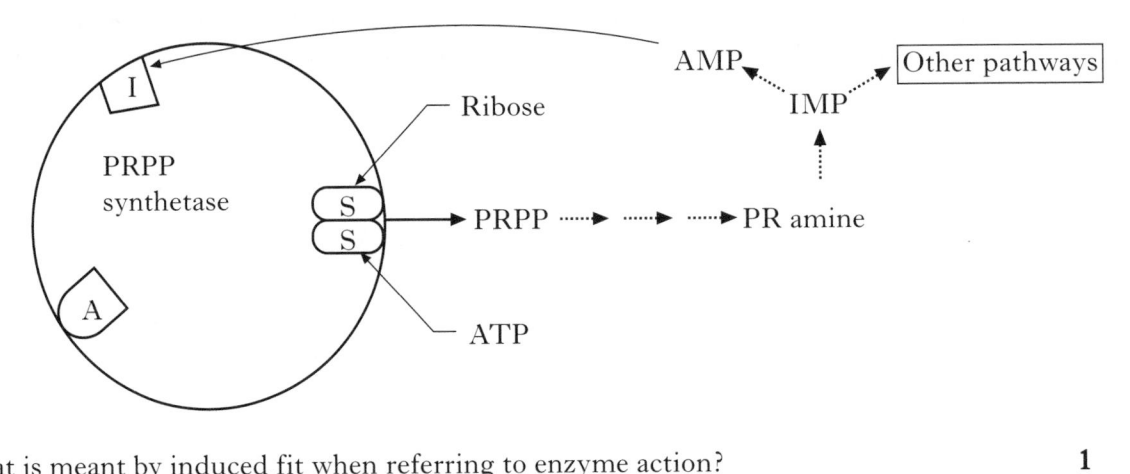

(*a*) What is meant by induced fit when referring to enzyme action? **1**

(*b*) Explain why PRPP synthetase is described as an allosteric enzyme. **1**

(*c*) Describe the effect of AMP formation on the metabolic pathway. **2**

(4)

Marks

5. The diagram below shows energy flow through a deciduous forest ecosystem. Units are kJ m^{-2} day^{-1}.

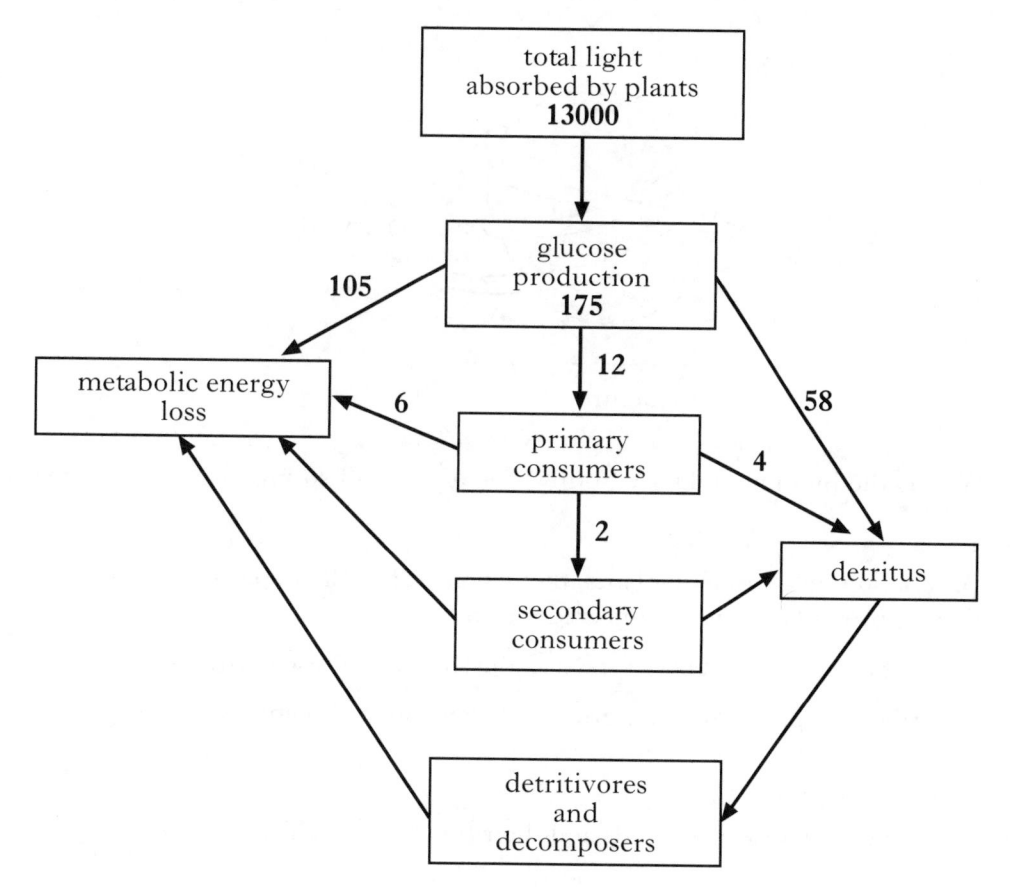

(a) Calculate the percentage of light energy that is captured in photosynthesis by the forest plants.

1

(b) What is the value for net primary productivity (NPP) in this ecosystem?

1

(c) Ten percent is often quoted as a typical value for ecological efficiency. Use the data to show that this value does not always apply to energy transfer between trophic levels.

1

(d) In what form is the energy lost from metabolism?

1

(e) Compare the use of digestive enzymes by detritivores and decomposers.

1

(5)

Marks

6. The figure below shows processes in the nitrogen cycle that rely on the activities of micro-organisms.

(a) The bacteria responsible for processes Q and R are *obligate aerobes*.

What does this term suggest about their metabolic requirements?　1

(b) Nitrogen fixation is often the product of a prokaryote–eukaryote symbiosis.
It depends on the action of an enzyme system that functions best in anaerobic conditions.

(i) Identify a prokaryote involved in such an interaction.　1

(ii) Name the enzyme responsible for nitrogen fixation.　1

(iii) What is the role of leghaemoglobin in this interaction?　1

(c) State the likely effect of process S on soil fertility in aerobic conditions.　1

(5)

7. Rust fungi are pathogens of many monocultures. In infected plants, *pustules* are formed that are responsible for the spread of infection.

The figure below shows the spread of a rust fungus from a single infected plant.

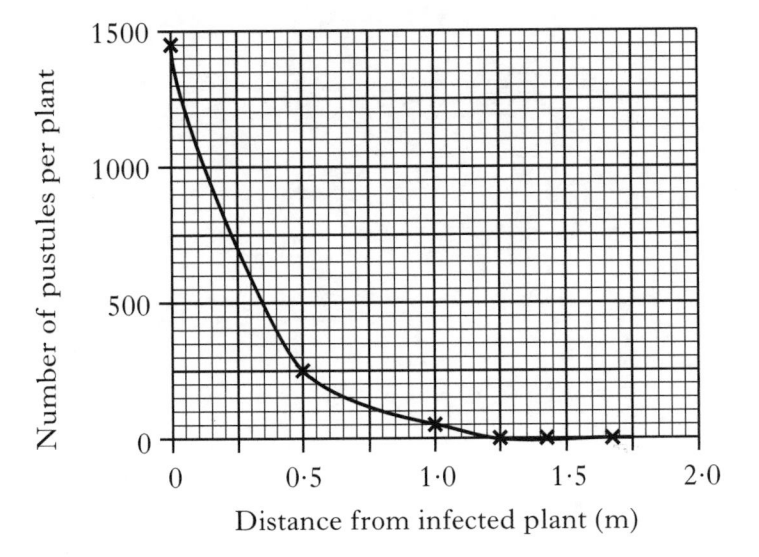

(a) Define the term monoculture.　1

(b) What do the data suggest about the spacing needed to prevent the fungus infection from spreading?　1

(c) Apart from altering spacing, suggest another way of growing rust-free crops.　1

(3)

Marks

8. Answer **either** A **or** B.

 A. Discuss how ecosystems may be affected by the following:

   (i) phosphate enrichment;　　5

   (ii) exotic species;　　4

   (iii) persistent toxic pollutants.　　6

 OR　　**(15)**

 B. Discuss the roles of the following in the survival of organisms:

   (i) dormancy;　　7

   (ii) mimicry;　　4

   (iii) mutualism.　　4

　　(15)

[END OF SECTION B]

SECTION C

Candidates should attempt questions on <u>one</u> unit, <u>either</u> Biotechnology <u>or</u> Animal Behaviour <u>or</u> Physiology, Health and Exercise.

The questions on Animal Behaviour can be found on pages 20–22.

The questions on Physiology, Health and Exercise can be found on pages 23–25.

All answers must be written clearly and legibly in ink.

Labelled diagrams may be used where appropriate.

Marks

Biotechnology

1. (a) The Figure below shows the growth curve of a bacterium.

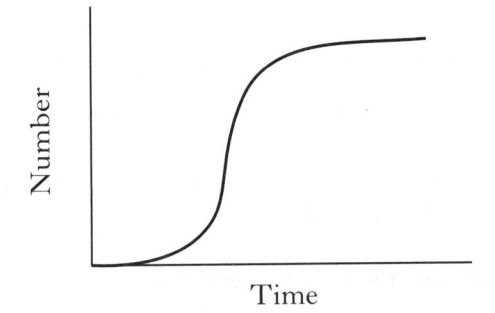

Give **two** reasons why there is only a small change in the number of bacteria during the lag phase.   **2**

(b) A haemocytometer is used to estimate cell numbers. The diagram below shows part of a haemocytometer grid. The depth of the chamber is 0·1 mm.

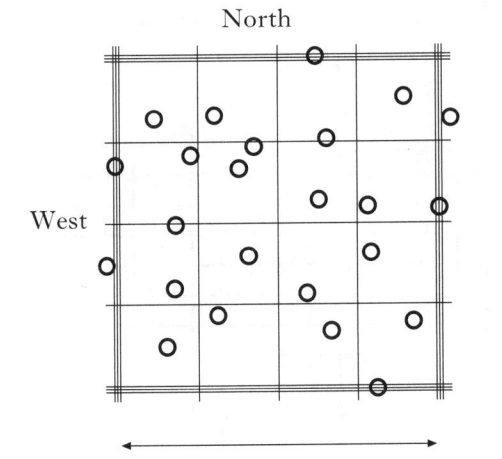

        0·2 mm

    (i) One precaution taken when using the grid is to exclude cells overlapping the north and west sides.

        What is the purpose of this precaution?   **1**

    (ii) Calculate the number of cells in 1 mm³ of the sample shown on the haemocytometer grid.   **1**

  (c) (i) Penicillin is an antibiotic that is described as *bacteriostatic*.

        Distinguish between *bacteriostatic* activity and *bactericidal* activity.   **1**

    (ii) Name an antibiotic other than penicillin.   **1**

  (d) Antibodies are produced in response to the presence of foreign antigens.

    (i) Name the cells that secrete antibodies.   **1**

    (ii) Give **one** medical use of monoclonal antibodies.   **1**

                                   (8)

Biotechnology **(continued)**

Marks

2. Explain how genetic modification of the *"flavrsavr"* tomato plant has resulted in fruit with longer shelf life.

(4)

3. (*a*) The nitrogen content of two yeast extracts, BW6 and BK1, is shown in the Table below.

	Yeast extract	
	BW6	*BK1*
Total nitrogen (g/100 g)	7·1	11·9
% of nitrogen as amino acids	34	56

The figure below shows the effect on the growth of the bacterium *Lactobacillus casei* of adding different proportions of BW6 and BK1.

Figure: Effect of varying proportions of BW6 and BK1 on the growth of *L. casei*

(i) Use the data to describe the effect of varying the proportions of the extracts on the growth of the bacterium.

2

(ii) Suggest a reason for this effect on *L. casei*.

1

(*b*) Give one agricultural use of *Lactobacillus* species.

1

(4)

Biotechnology **(continued)**   *Marks*

4.   Different yeast species are cultured to create large quantities of yeast cell biomass. Some of the biomass is destined for activities such as brewing and baking while much of the biomass is treated to bring about autolysis. The *autolysate* produced has a variety of uses, for example as a nutrient source in fermentation media.

    (*a*) What is meant by the term *autolysis*?   **1**

    (*b*) State **two** factors that could influence the characteristics of yeast autolysate.   **2**

    (*c*) Yeast extract is prepared from the autolysate.

       State one use of yeast extract in the food industry.   **1**

                                                                          (4)

                                                                        (20)

[End of *Biotechnology* questions. *Animal Behaviour* questions start on Page 20]

[Turn over

SECTION C (continued)   *Marks*

Animal Behaviour

1. The woodlouse *Hemilepistus reaumuri* lives in deserts. To avoid drying out, it digs a burrow from which it ventures each day to forage.

   Figure: Life cycle of *H. reaumuri*

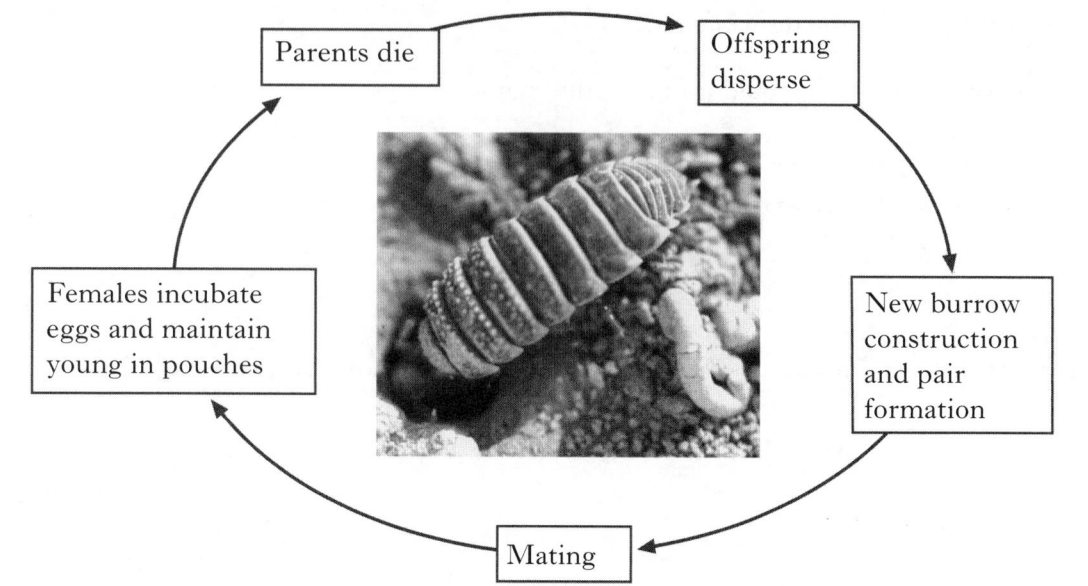

   (a) After dispersal, both males and females can begin new burrows, or they can attempt to pair with an existing burrower.

   Why are larger males more successful than smaller ones in pair formation with a female that has already started a burrow?   1

   (b) Suggest proximate and ultimate causes for burrow digging in this species.   2

   (c) For *H. reaumuri*, state one reason why the parental investment of females is higher than that of males.   1

   (d) After foraging, these woodlice show an *innate* ability to navigate straight back to their burrows.

   What is meant by the term innate?   1

   (e) State the effect of an increased encounter rate and a reduced handling time on the duration of foraging.   1

        (6)

Animal Behaviour **(continued)**   *Marks*

2. The fire ant *Solenopsis invicta* is a social insect found in South America. A study of kin selection showed that colonies of *S. invicta* can have either of two distinct social structures, *compact* colonies or *sprawling* colonies.

   Compact colonies contain ants that are all produced by a single female, the queen. The workers in compact colonies are loyal to the queen and are aggressive towards intruders. In contrast, large sprawling colonies, which are becoming more common, are formed from many interconnected nests inhabited by many queens.

   The difference in social structure depends on the presence or absence of allele B of the gene *GP-9*. Ants with the B allele produce a receptor protein that enables them to distinguish the odours of ants from different genetic backgrounds.

   (*a*) What is meant by the term *kin selection*?   1

   (*b*) Allele B is only found in compact colonies.

        Explain how the absence of allele B has led to the formation of the sprawling colony.   2

   (*c*) Give another example of a single gene effect.   1

                                                                (4)

3. Discuss the role of dispersal in the avoidance of inbreeding in birds and mammals.

   Why is it important for animals to avoid inbreeding and how is this achieved?   **(4)**

[Turn over

Animal Behaviour **(continued)**   *Marks*

4. The success of herring gull (*Larus argentatus*) foraging behaviour was studied using video recordings. Herring gulls have adult plumage after 4 years; the age of younger birds can be determined by other visible characteristics.

The Figure shows the mean feeding rates for herring gulls in different age classes.

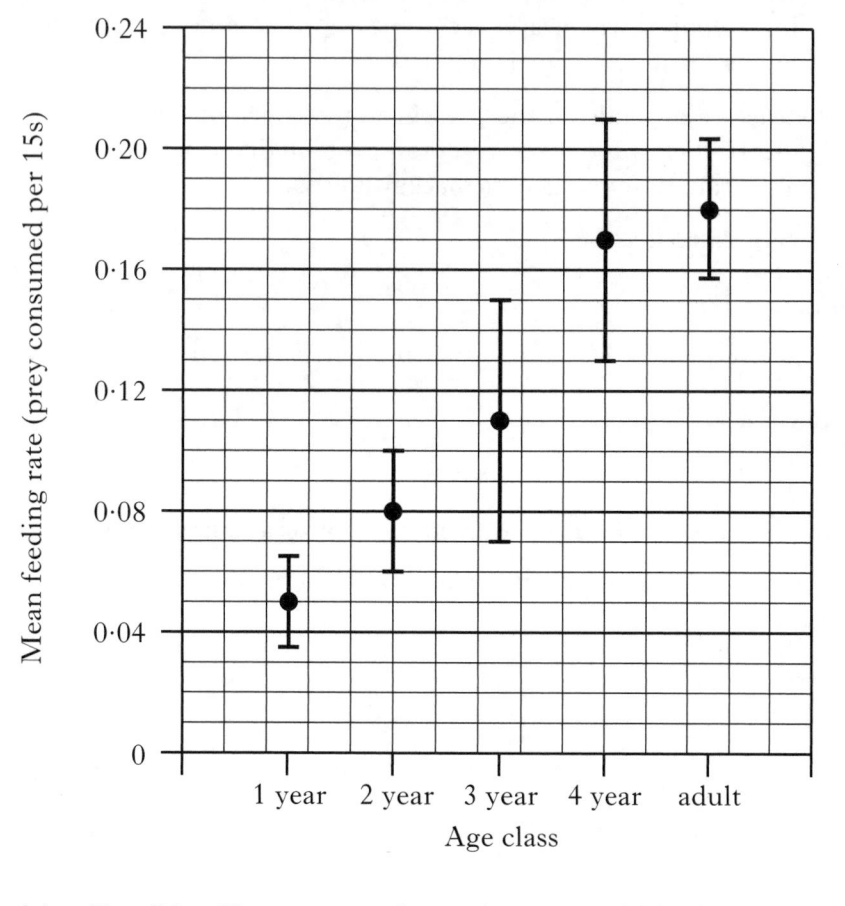

(*a*) (i)   Identify **two** age classes between which there is a significant difference in foraging success.   1

(ii) Suggest an explanation for the trend seen in the feeding rate.   1

(iii) An adult feeding at 0·18 prey per 15 seconds takes 83 seconds to capture one prey item.

How long would it take a one-year-old to capture one prey item?   1

(*b*) Suggest **one** advantage of using video recording for this analysis.   1

(*c*) Describe **two** ways in which herring gulls have successfully adapted to human influence.   2

                                                                                                    (6)

                                                                                                    (20)

[End of *Animal Behaviour* questions. *Physiology, Health and Exercise* questions start on Page 23]

SECTION C (continued)   *Marks*

Physiology, Health and Exercise

1.   A stent is a narrow, wire mesh tube that can be inserted into a blood vessel. It may be used to treat atherosclerosis in the blood vessels of the heart. Figure 1 shows a blood vessel before and after the procedure to insert a stent.

   Figure 1

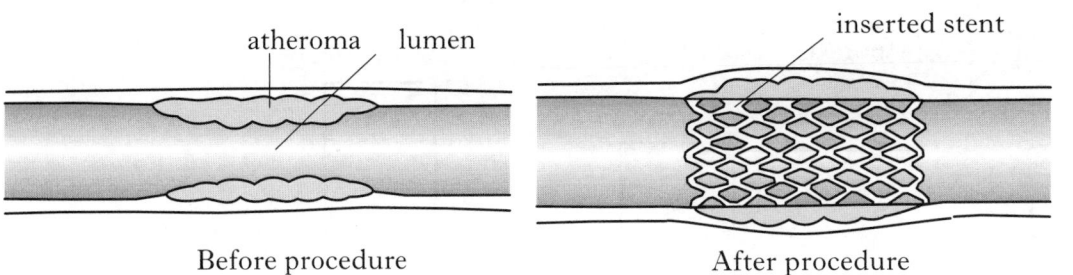

      Before procedure   After procedure

   (*a*) Name the blood vessels that deliver blood to the myocardium.   1

   (*b*) Describe how *atherosclerosis* develops.   2

   (*c*) Figure 2 shows the volume changes in a blood vessel in the heart as a result of a stent being fitted.

   Figure 2

      (i)   Use the data to explain how the procedure achieves increased blood flow.   2

      (ii) What term is used for the chest pain relieved by this procedure?   1

                                                                                       (6)

                                                                              [Turn over

Physiology, Health and Exercise **(continued)**   *Marks*

2. The data show trends expected in the numbers of American women who have low bone mass and who will go on to develop osteoporosis.

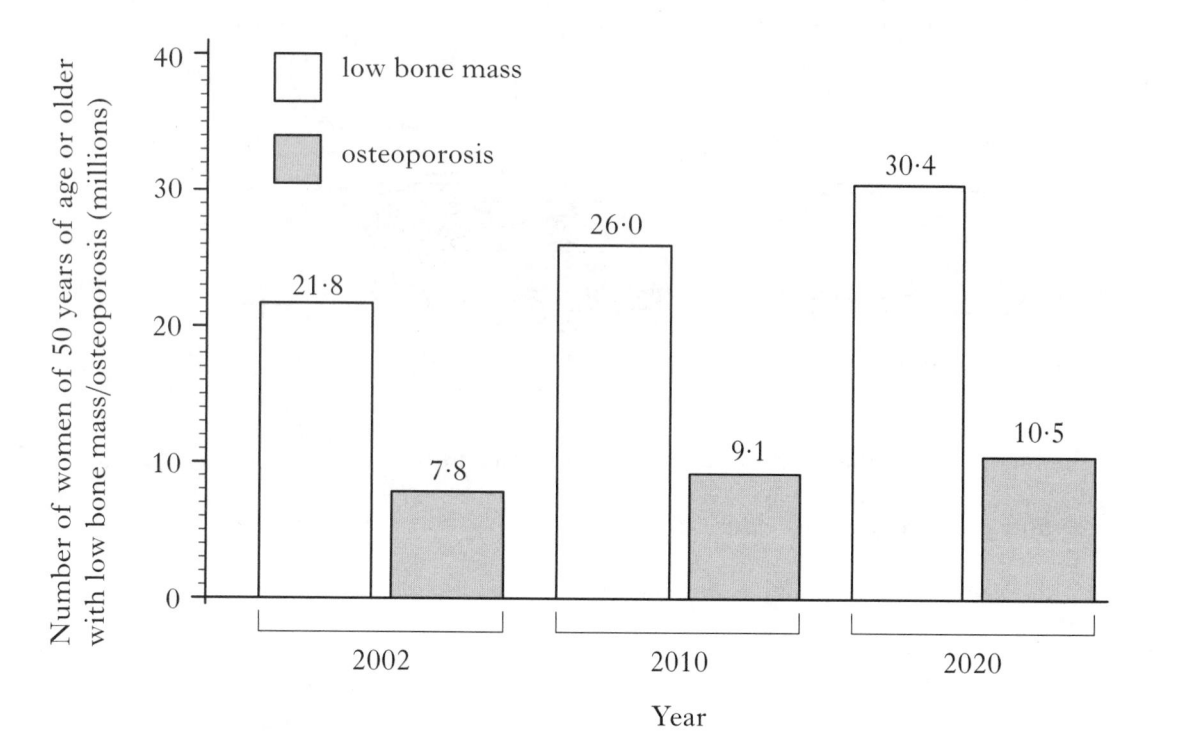

(*a*) Give one feature of osteoporosis other than low bone mass.   1

(*b*) Explain why the study focuses on women of 50 years of age or older.   1

(*c*) Authors of the research claimed that:

   "*In future, fewer American women with hip problems will eventually go on to develop osteoporosis.*"

   (i)   Suggest how critics could use the data provided to contradict this claim.   1

   (ii) How did the authors use the data to arrive at their conclusion?   1

(*d*) Explain why American teenagers would be advised to take up jogging rather than swimming to reduce the risk of osteoporosis.   2

                                                                                                                (6)

Physiology, Health and Exercise **(continued)**   *Marks*

3. (*a*) The table shows data relating to four members of a group trying to achieve different weight-loss targets. The energy deficit value indicates the severity of their intended diet. Dietary weight loss is assumed to be from fat loss.

A negative energy balance of 29·4 MJ is required to lose 1 kg.

Group member	*Present weight* (kg)	*Target weight* (kg)	*Energy deficit* (MJ/day)
A	96	91	2
B	121	113	3
C	104	98	2
D	92	82	3

   (i)   How many days will individual **D** take to reach the target weight?   1

   (ii) Individual **A** is 1·74m in height. Calculate this individual's body mass index (BMI).   1

   (*b*) Explain why being "overweight" does not always mean that someone is unhealthy.   1

   (*c*) Name a method of measuring body composition.   1

                                                                        (4)

4. Discuss the use of exercise testing in the assessment of aerobic fitness.   **(4)**

                                                                        (20)

[END OF QUESTION PAPER]

[BLANK PAGE]

2009

[BLANK PAGE]

X007/701

| NATIONAL QUALIFICATIONS 2009 | THURSDAY, 28 MAY 1.00 PM – 3.30 PM | BIOLOGY ADVANCED HIGHER |

SECTION A–Questions 1—25 (25 marks)

Instructions for completion of Section A are given on *Page two*.

SECTIONS B AND C

The answer to each question should be written in ink in the answer book provided. Any additional paper (if used) should be placed inside the front cover of the answer book.

Rough work should be scored through.

Section B (55 marks)

All questions should be attempted. Candidates should note that Question 8 contains a choice.

Question 1 is on Pages 10, 11 and 12. Questions 2, 3 and 4 are on Page 13. Pages 12 and 13 are fold-out pages.

Section C (20 marks)

Candidates should attempt the questions in **one** unit, **either** Biotechnology **or** Animal Behaviour **or** Physiology, Health and Exercise.

Read carefully

1   Check that the answer sheet provided is for **Biology Advanced Higher (Section A)**.

2   For this section of the examination you must use an **HB pencil** and, where necessary, an eraser.

3   Check that the answer sheet you have been given has **your name**, **date of birth**, **SCN** (Scottish Candidate Number) and **Centre Name** printed on it.

     Do not change any of these details.

4   If any of this information is wrong, tell the Invigilator immediately.

5   If this information is correct, **print** your name and seat number in the boxes provided.

6   The answer to each question is **either** A, B, C or D. Decide what your answer is, then, using your pencil, put a horizontal line in the space provided (see sample question below).

7   There is **only one correct** answer to each question.

8   Any rough working should be done on the question paper or the rough working sheet, **not** on your answer sheet.

9   At the end of the exam, put the **answer sheet for Section A inside the front cover of the answer book**.

Sample Question

Which of the following molecules contains six carbon atoms?

A   Glucose

B   Pyruvic acid

C   Ribulose bisphosphate

D   Acetyl coenzyme A

The correct answer is **A**—Glucose. The answer **A** has been clearly marked in **pencil** with a horizontal line (see below).

Changing an answer

If you decide to change your answer, carefully erase your first answer and using your pencil, fill in the answer you want. The answer below has been changed to **D**.

SECTION A

All questions in this section should be attempted.

Answers should be given on the separate answer sheet provided.

1. The diagram shows a bacterial cell.

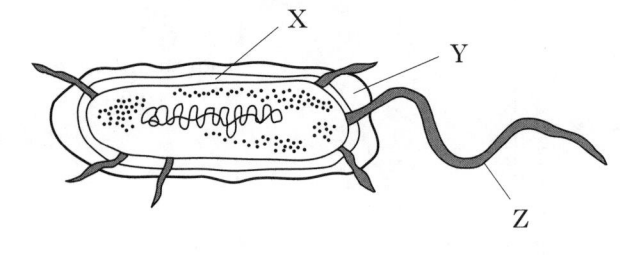

Which line in the table below correctly identifies the labelled structures?

	X	Y	Z
A	cell wall	capsule	flagellum
B	capsule	cell wall	flagellum
C	cell wall	capsule	pilus
D	capsule	cell wall	pilus

2. Which of the following diagrams best represents the sequence of phases involved in the cell cycle?

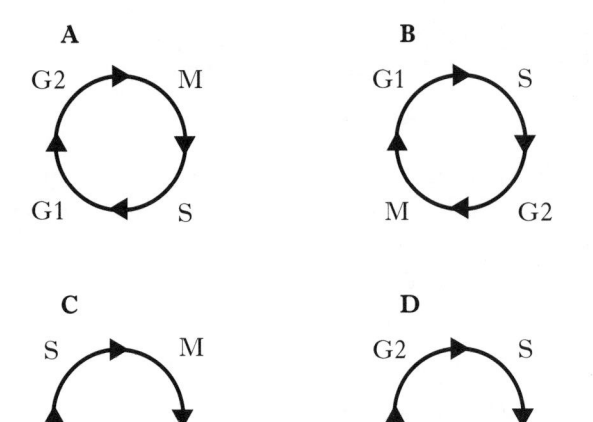

3. The covalent chemical bonds between nucleotides in DNA are

  A peptide

  B phosphodiester

  C glycosidic

  D hydrogen.

4. Which line in the table below classifies correctly the four bases in DNA as either purines or pyrimidines?

	Purines	Pyrimidines
A	adenine and thymine	cytosine and guanine
B	cytosine and guanine	adenine and thymine
C	cytosine and thymine	adenine and guanine
D	adenine and guanine	cytosine and thymine

5. The table below shows the number of cells from a cell culture at different points in the cell cycle.

Stage	Number of cells
Interphase	462
Prophase	23
Metaphase	24
Anaphase	4
Telophase	16

The mitotic index of the sample is

  A 14·5%

  B 12·7%

  C 85·5%

  D 74·7%.

[Turn over

6. The percentage of adenine bases in a double stranded DNA molecule is 30% and in a single stranded RNA molecule it is 25%.

Which line in the table below shows the number of other bases in each molecule for which the percentage could be calculated?

	RNA	DNA
A	none	three
B	none	none
C	one	two
D	one	three

7. During a biochemical reaction the transfer of a phosphate group from one molecule to another is catalysed by

A   ligase

B   ATPase

C   kinase

D   nuclease.

8. The diagram below shows an enzyme-catalysed reaction.

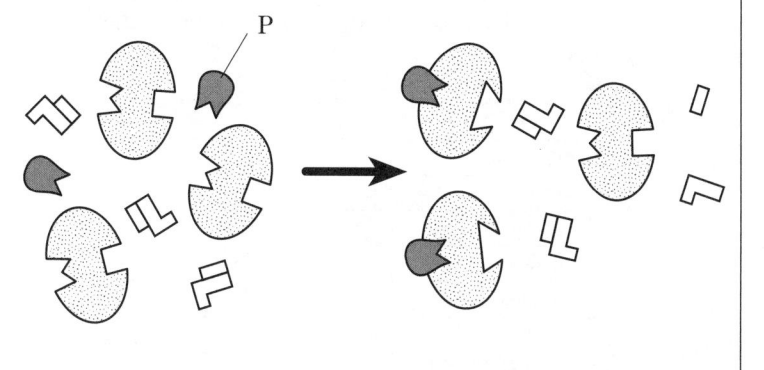

Which of the following correctly identifies molecule P?

A   Substrate

B   Activator

C   Competitive inhibitor

D   Non-competitive inhibitor

9. The diagram below shows the changes in the activity of enzymes that synthesise tryptophan and utilise lactose in a cell after the addition of tryptophan and lactose.

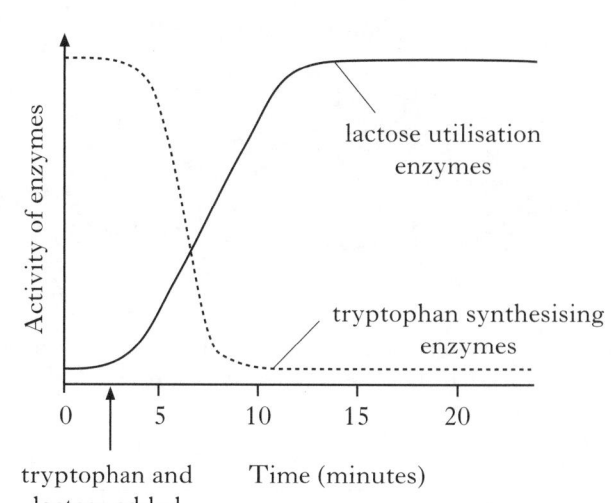

What valid conclusion may be made from the graph?

A   Addition of lactose acts as a negative enzyme modulator.

B   Addition of tryptophan acts as a positive enzyme modulator.

C   Enzyme induction is occurring in lactose utilisation enzymes.

D   Enzyme induction is occurring in tryptophan synthesising enzymes.

10. During the production of transgenic plants, which of the following bacteria would be used to transfer recombinant plasmids into plant protoplasts?

A   *Agrobacterium*

B   *E. coli*

C   *Pseudomonas*

D   *Rhizobium*

11. The diagram below shows the restriction enzyme sites in a plasmid that carries the genes for resistance to the antibiotics ampicillin and tetracycline.

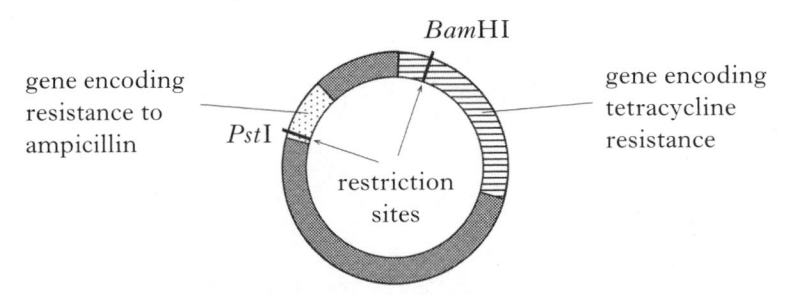

Which line in the table below identifies correctly the antibiotic resistance that would remain when a gene is inserted at these restriction enzyme sites?

	Gene inserted into restriction enzyme site	Antibiotic resistance remaining
A	BamHI	tetracycline and ampicillin
B	PstI	ampicillin
C	PstI	tetracycline and ampicillin
D	BamHI	ampicillin

12. A piece of DNA was digested using the restriction enzymes BamHI and EcoRI. The results are shown below.

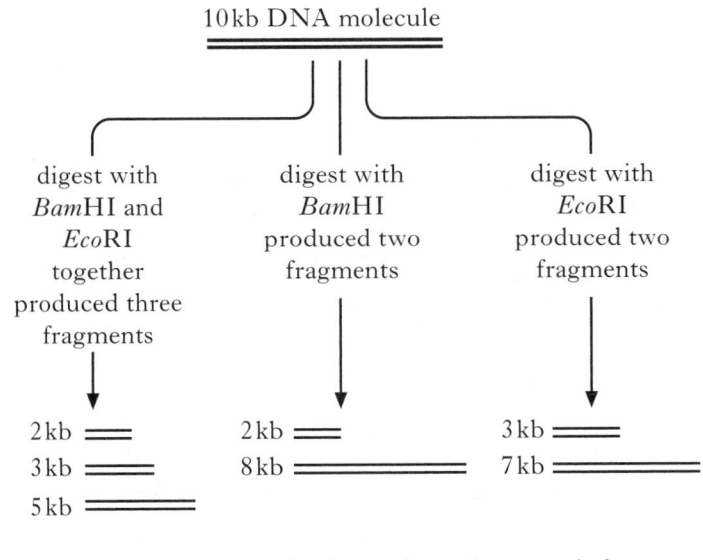

Which of the following restriction maps can be drawn from these results?

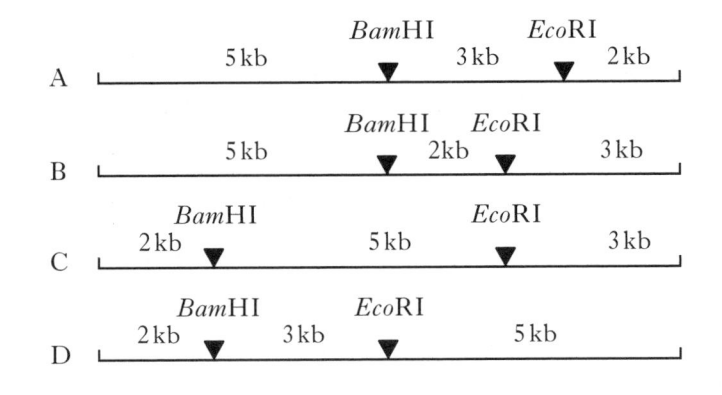

13. The graph below shows variation in biomass throughout one year in an aquatic ecosystem.

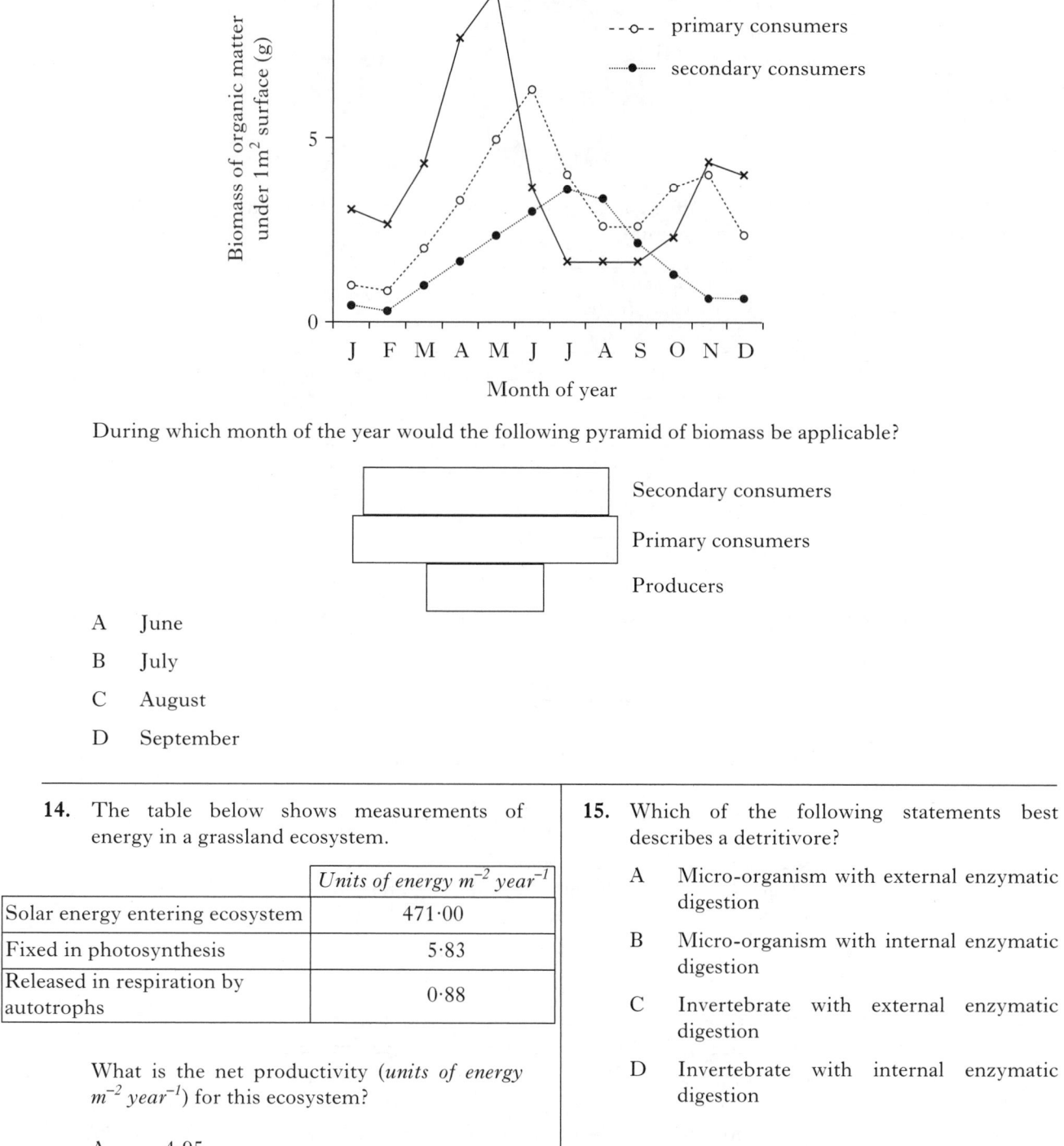

During which month of the year would the following pyramid of biomass be applicable?

Secondary consumers

Primary consumers

Producers

A　June

B　July

C　August

D　September

14. The table below shows measurements of energy in a grassland ecosystem.

	Units of energy m^{-2} $year^{-1}$
Solar energy entering ecosystem	471·00
Fixed in photosynthesis	5·83
Released in respiration by autotrophs	0·88

What is the net productivity (units of energy m^{-2} $year^{-1}$) for this ecosystem?

A　　4·95

B　　6·71

C　　465·17

D　　470·12

15. Which of the following statements best describes a detritivore?

A　Micro-organism with external enzymatic digestion

B　Micro-organism with internal enzymatic digestion

C　Invertebrate with external enzymatic digestion

D　Invertebrate with internal enzymatic digestion

16. The release of nutrients from the remains of dead organisms in the soil is called

A　assimilation

B　humus formation

C　mineralisation

D　nitrification.

17. Which of the following promotes the loss of nitrogen from soil due to the activity of denitrifying bacteria?

A   Leaching of nitrate from soil in drainage water

B   Anaerobic conditions caused by water saturation

C   High levels of phosphate from addition of fertilisers

D   The presence of a leguminous crop such as clover

18. A flask containing a solution of ammonium salts was set up to demonstrate the activity of some of the micro-organisms involved in the nitrogen cycle. A sample of fresh soil was added to the solution and the concentration of nitrite measured over several weeks. The results are shown in the graph below.

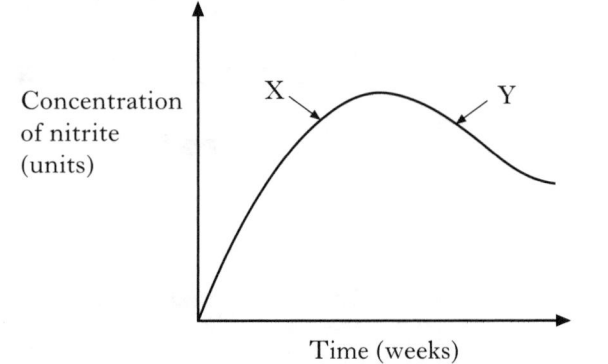

Concentration of nitrite (units)

Time (weeks)

Which line in the table below correctly represents bacterial activity which can account for the changes shown at X and Y?

	Bacteria active at X	Bacteria active at Y
A	Nitrosomonas	Rhizobium
B	Nitrobacter	Nitrosomonas
C	Nitrobacter	Rhizobium
D	Nitrosomonas	Nitrobacter

19. Coral snakes are highly venomous and have a pattern of dark red, yellow and black bands.

This is an example of

A   aposematic colouration

B   Batesian mimicry

C   camouflage

D   Mullerian mimicry.

20. A species of Latin American ant inhabits the thorns of a species of Acacia. The ant receives nectar and shelter from the plant. The plant receives protection from the ants.

This is an example of

A   parasitism

B   commensalism

C   mutualism

D   predation.

21. Hydra is a small freshwater animal that uses its tentacles to catch food. One variety (green hydra) has photosynthetic algae living in its tissues. Another variety (colourless hydra) has no algae.

mouth

tentacle

The relationship between Hydra and the algae is believed to be an example of mutualism.

Under what conditions would a comparison of the growth rates of green and colourless Hydra test this hypothesis?

A   Light; food supplied

B   Light; no food supplied

C   Dark; food supplied

D   Dark; no food supplied.

[Turn over

22. Animals may interact with their environment by conformation or regulation. Each statement below applies to one of these interactions.

1 A wide range of habitats can be occupied.
2 A restricted range of habitats can be occupied.
3 There is a high energy cost.
4 There is no energy cost.

Which statements apply to regulation?

A   1 and 3 only

B   1 and 4 only

C   2 and 3 only

D   2 and 4 only

23. The graph below shows primary productivity in a loch at different depths. Data were collected before and after an experiment in which phosphate was added to the loch.

Key
before phosphate added ------
after phosphate added ————

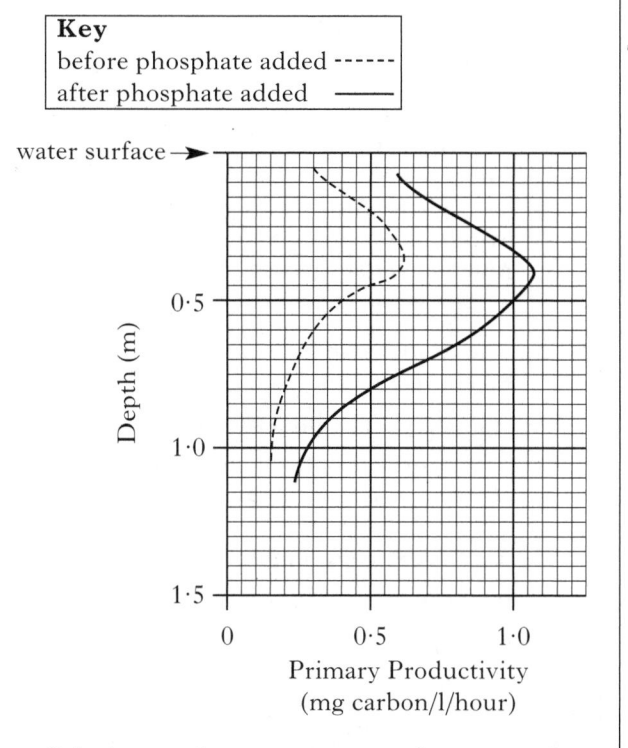

Calculate the percentage increase in productivity at a depth of 0·5 m that results from the addition of phosphate.

A   60%

B   75%

C   150%

D   300%

24. Which line in the table correctly identifies the effect of each pollutant?

	Biomagnification	Eutrophication	Global warming
A	phosphate	DDT	CFCs
B	DDT	phosphate	CFCs
C	CFCs	phosphate	DDT
D	DDT	CFCs	phosphate

25. The concentrations of some toxic organic chemicals in sea water were compared to concentrations known to produce lethal effects in laboratory experiments.

Which of the following is a valid conclusion from the data shown?

A   All the toxic organic chemicals are found at lethal concentrations in sea water.

B   Trichlorethylene is the only chemical found at lethal concentrations in sea water.

C   DDT produces toxic effects in sea water due to biomagnification through the ecosystem.

D   There is no evidence that the concentrations of toxic organic chemicals in sea water could produce lethal effects.

[END OF SECTION A]

Candidates are reminded that the answer sheet MUST be returned INSIDE the front cover of the answer book.

[Turn over for Section B on *Page ten*]

SECTION B

All questions in this section should be attempted.
All answers must be written clearly and legibly in ink.

1. The effects of large carnivores on ecosystems are not well understood. Predators can have a "top-down" effect that ripples down through the trophic levels below them. The effect is called a *trophic cascade*. In a trophic cascade a predatory species significantly affects consumer populations, which in turn results in significant changes at the producer level. Two recent studies in the USA have investigated trophic cascades.

    One study investigated the effects of reintroducing wolves (*Canis lupus*) to Yellowstone National Park in 1994. The strength of the trophic cascade was assessed by measuring feeding damage caused by elk (*Cervus elaphus*) to saplings produced by regenerating aspen trees (*Populus tremuloides*) (Table 1).

    In the second study, a trophic cascade was quantified in a comparison of two neighbouring canyons in Zion National Park. These two canyons, Zion Canyon and North Creek, have similar geology, climate and plant species but are visited by substantially different numbers of tourists. The Figure shows the age structure of populations of cottonwood trees (*Populus fremontii*) in the two canyons. The age of cottonwood trees was estimated by measuring their diameter at chest height. Other than the trees, the most significant species within the community are the predatory cougar (*Puma concolor*) and the herbivorous mule deer (*Odocoileus hemionus*).

    To compare the abundance of these species in the two canyons, data were collected from two-metre-wide transects following the course of river and stream banks. Evidence of cougars, which are highly sensitive to human disturbance, was determined by searching for scats (droppings) along 4000m of walking trails in the two localities (Table 2).

Table 1 : Survey data for Yellowstone National Park

Year	Wolf population	Elk population	Feeding damage (%)	Average aspen sapling height (cm)
1993	0	17 500	No data	No data
1997	24	13 000	95	30
2001	74	12 000	80	50
2005	82	9000	20	170

Question 1 (continued)

Figure: Age structure of cottonwood trees in two canyons in Zion National Park

Number of trees of each age group per kilometre

Table 2: Comparative data for three species in Zion National Park

Species	Canyon	
	North Creek	Zion Canyon
Cougar (scats per km)	1·75	0
Deer (hoof prints per km)	3·3	700
Young cottonwood (saplings per km)	900	23

[Question 1 continues on *Page twelve*

Question 1 (continued)

Marks

(a) Top-down effects are caused by heterotrophs. What is meant by the term heterotroph?   **1**

(b) Using data from Table 1:

   (i) describe the trophic cascade caused by the reintroduction of wolves;   **2**

   (ii) calculate the percentage increase in wolf population over the period 1997 to 2001;   **1**

   (iii) suggest **one** reason why the herbivore population declined by less than 8% over the same period.   **1**

(c) Compare the abundance of old and young cottonwood trees in North Creek and Zion Canyon.   **2**

(d) Suggest why the investigators used cougar scats rather than sightings to estimate cougar abundance.   **1**

(e) Zion Canyon has been accessible to a large number of tourists since the 1930s, whereas North Creek is rarely visited. Justify the conclusion that, by influencing the trophic cascade, tourism is responsible for the poor survival of young cottonwoods.   **2**

(f) (i) What term describes biotic effects that increase in intensity as the population in an area increases?   **1**

   (ii) Explain how the intensity of grazing can influence the *diversity* of plant species.   **2**

(13)

[Questions 2, 3 and 4 are on fold-out *Page thirteen*

Marks

2. (a) Himalayan balsam (*Impatiens glandulifera*) is an exotic species that spread into Scotland after being introduced into the UK in 1839. Left unchecked it can form an ecologically harmful monoculture. Himalayan balsam is an annual plant (its whole life cycle takes place within one year). Seeds of this species can remain dormant in the soil for up to two years.

    (i) What is the benefit of a period of dormancy in seeds?   1

    (ii) Describe a damaging effect arising from the spread of an exotic species.   1

    (iii) Suggest a method for controlling Himalayan balsam.   1

    (iv) How would the seed dormancy of the Himalayan balsam affect the design of an eradication programme?   1

(b) Give **one** effect on soil when monoculture is used in intensive food production.   1

           (5)

3. Explain how the use of fossil fuels disrupts the symbiotic relationship in coral.   **(4)**

4. (a) Why is competition regarded as a negative interaction?   1

  (b) Explain what is meant by a fundamental niche.   1

  (c) A survey of birds in the Bismarck Islands, Papua New Guinea, found that two similar species of cuckoo-doves, *Macropygia mackinlayi* and *M. nigrirostris*, are never found breeding on the same island.

       M. mackinlayi   *M. nigrirostris*

    The two species are believed to have very similar fundamental niches. Suggest an explanation for the two species occupying different islands.   2

  (d) Parasites may be transmitted between closely related species.

    (i) Why is the transmission of parasites less common between **unrelated** species?   1

    (ii) State **one** way in which parasites can be transmitted.   1

           (6)

Marks

5. The diagram below shows a section of plasma membrane with proteins labelled A to E.

(a) (i) Identify which of the proteins A to E are integral membrane proteins. **1**

(ii) Which type of signalling molecule requires a receptor protein at the cell surface? **1**

(b) The membranes of most eukaryotic cells contain a proportion of the steroid cholesterol.

(i) Describe the general structure of a steroid. **1**

(ii) State **one** role of cholesterol in membranes. **1**

(iii) The table below shows the proportion of cholesterol in membranes from different locations.

Membrane location	Proportion of cholesterol (g cholesterol per g membrane)
Liver plasma membrane	0·18
Mitochondrial membrane	0·03
Endoplasmic reticulum	0·06

Show, as a simple whole number ratio, the relative amounts of cholesterol in liver plasma membrane, mitochondrial membrane and endoplasmic reticulum. **1**

(5)

Marks

6. Binding of specific proteins to DNA is important in the control of gene expression.

   (a) Describe the effect of repressor protein binding to DNA in the *lac* operon.   1

   (b) Binding to DNA of the *engrailed* protein of the fruit fly *Drosophila melanogaster* is required during development of the fruit fly embryo.

   The DNA-binding region of the engrailed protein consists of a stretch of sixty amino acids that contain two α-helices connected by a short extended chain of amino acids as shown in Figure 1.

   Figure 1

   (i) What level of protein structure is an α-helix?   1

   (ii) The side chains of the amino acids within the α-helix regions interact directly with DNA. Figure 2 shows the amino acids in a short stretch of one of the α-helix regions of the engrailed protein.

   Figure 2

   Name the class of amino acid to which lysine belongs.   1

   (iii) The binding region of the engrailed protein contains a high proportion of lysine residues. Suggest how the presence of these amino acids would assist in the binding of the engrailed protein to DNA.   1

   (4)

[Turn over

Marks

7. Enzyme kinetics is the study of the rate of enzyme-catalysed reactions.
The graph below shows the rates of the reaction for the enzyme penicillinase over a range of substrate concentrations. The substrate is penicillin.

Substrate concentration
(μmoles per litre)

The Michaelis constant (K_m) of an enzyme is the substrate concentration at which the reaction rate is half its maximum rate.

(a) Calculate the K_m of penicillinase assuming the graph shows that the maximum rate has been reached. **1**

(b) Explain why the K_m of an enzyme increases when a competitive inhibitor is present. **1**

(c) The turnover number of an enzyme is the number of substrate molecules converted into product by an enzyme in one second when an enzyme is working at its maximum rate. The turnover number for penicillinase is 2000 per second.

Calculate the time taken to catalyse the breakdown of one penicillin molecule. **1**

(3)

8. Answer **either** A **or** B.

A. Describe the structure of the monosaccharide glucose. Discuss the structures and functions of the main polysaccharides made using glucose as a monomer. **(15)**

OR

B. Give an account of the processes involved in the polymerase chain reaction (PCR) and DNA profiling. **(15)**

[*END OF SECTION B*]

SECTION C

Candidates should attempt questions on <u>one</u> unit, <u>either</u> Biotechnology <u>or</u> Animal Behaviour <u>or</u> Physiology, Health and Exercise.

The questions on Animal Behaviour can be found on pages 20–23.

The questions on Physiology, Health and Exercise can be found on pages 24–26.

All answers must be written clearly and legibly in ink.

Labelled diagrams may be used where appropriate.

Marks

BIOTECHNOLOGY

1. The Figure below shows the final stage in a test that confirms a blood sample contains antibodies against *Herpes simplex* virus (HSV). HSV antigen is attached to the plastic well and any unbound areas are coated with non-reactive material.

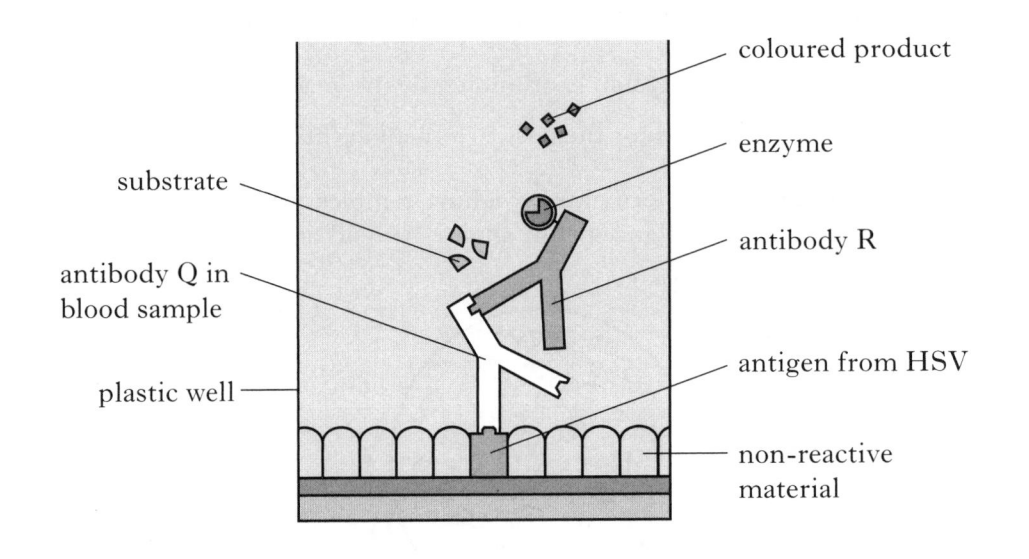

(a) (i) Identify the technique represented in the diagram.   1

   (ii) Explain why the test represented would not reveal if the person had been infected with chickenpox virus.   1

   (iii) Use information in the Figure to explain why inadequate rinsing just before the stage shown might result in a *false* positive result.   2

(b) Antibody R was produced commercially in a fermenter from hybridoma cells.

   What **two** cell types are combined to make hybridoma cells?   1

   (5)

[Turn over

BIOTECHNOLOGY (continued)

Marks

2. The flow chart shows steps involved in the manufacture of yoghurt.

(a) The milk mixture is heated to 95 °C for 20 minutes to remove dissolved oxygen.

   (i)   What chemical conversion is promoted by the anaerobic conditions?   1

   (ii) Give a further reason for the heat treatment at this stage.   1

(b) During incubation in the fermenter, yoghurt samples were removed and examined under a microscope. The figure below shows the field of view.

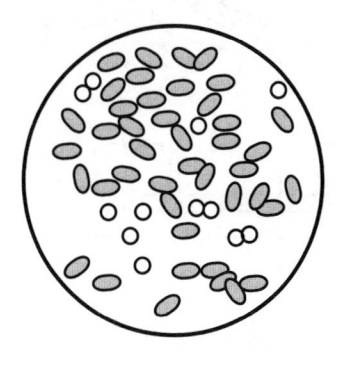

   (i)   What can be observed?   1

   (ii) Account for the observation.   1

   (4)

3. Describe the scaling up process required to produce a suitable volume of pure bacterial culture for an industrial fermenter.   **(5)**

BIOTECHNOLOGY (continued)   *Marks*

4.   Silage is used for winter feeding of farm animals and is commonly made by wrapping baled grass in polythene. Ensilage of plants in this way preserves the nutritional quality by limiting protein breakdown.

(a) Apart from wrapping bales, give **one** other method of making silage.   1

(b) Explain how changes that take place within the wrapped bale help to preserve the silage.   2

(c) Name a bacterial species that would be added before the baled grass is wrapped.   1

(d) In a study involving ensilage of harvested lupin plants, researchers evaluated the effect of adding bacteria to the bales. The graphs below show the data obtained. Error bars show variation between replicates.

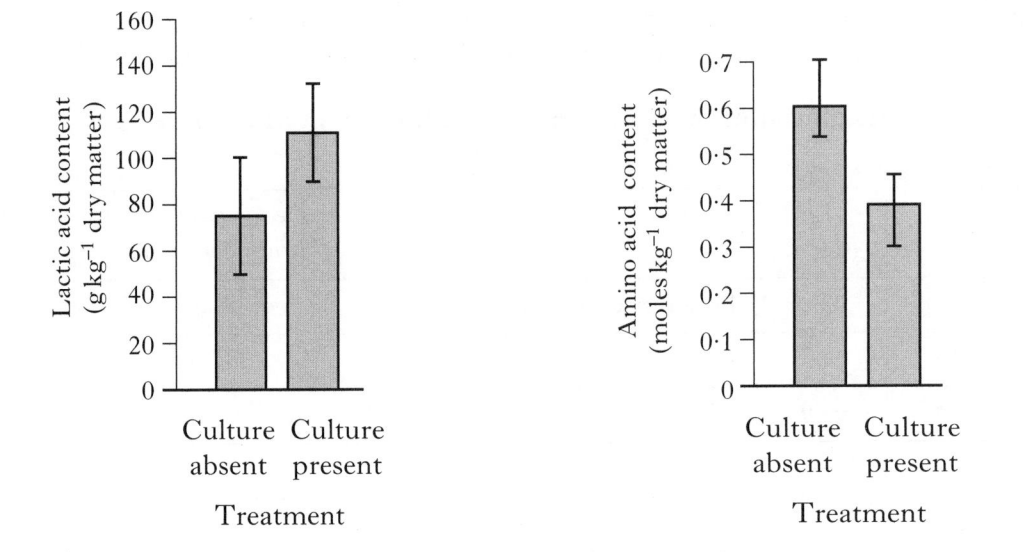

(i)   What evidence supports the conclusion that the treatment with bacteria preserves the nutritional quality of the plant material?   1

(ii) Draw **one** other conclusion about the effect of adding bacteria to fermenting silage.   1

                                                                                              (6)

                                                                                              (20)

[End of *Biotechnology* questions. *Animal Behaviour* questions start on Page 20]

SECTION C (continued)　　　　　　　　　　　*Marks*

ANIMAL BEHAVIOUR

1.　The eastern spinebill (*Acanthorhyncus tenuirostris*) is a small bird from eastern Australia. One of its major foods is nectar from the mountain correa (*Correa lawrenciana*).

Figure 1:　Eastern spinebill feeding on mountain correa

　(*a*)　In a study of eastern spinebill foraging, flowers of mountain correa were assigned to different developmental stages (Floral stages 1–5). Some characteristics of each stage are shown in the Table. Figure 2 shows the abundance of floral stages available and the foraging choices made by eastern spinebills feeding on the flowers.

Table:　Characteristics of mountain correa flowers at different stages

Floral stage	Age (days)	Pollen production	Volume of nectar produced per flower over 24 hours (μl)
1	1–2	Pollen present, not released	1·0
2	3–7	Pollen released	3·1
3	8–9	Little, if any, pollen present	0·5
4	10–13	No pollen	0
5	14+	No pollen	0

ANIMAL BEHAVIOUR (continued)   *Marks*

1. (*a*) (continued)

Figure 2: **Proportions of floral stages available and foraging choices made by eastern spinebills**

(i)   Use the data in Figure 2 to compare floral stages 2 and 5.   2

(ii)   What is meant by the term optimal foraging?   1

(iii) How does the information provided in both the Table and Figure 2
       demonstrate optimal foraging in spinebills?   1

(*b*) The eastern spinebill's nest is a small cup made mainly from twigs, grass, bark,
       feathers and spider webs. Only the female builds the nest and incubates the eggs but
       both parents feed the young after they have hatched.

(i)   This information suggests greater investment by the female parent. Describe
       another way in which female investment is likely to be greater than that of the
       male parent.   1

(ii)   Explain how nest building in the eastern spinebill provides an example of an
       extended phenotype.   1

(*c*) The eastern spinebill does not show any marked sexual dimorphism.

       Figure 1 shows a male bird. What would the female bird look like in comparison?   1

                                                                                 (7)

                                                                        [Turn over

ANIMAL BEHAVIOUR (continued)

Marks

2. The silk produced by female spiders often contains chemical deposits that provide males with important information about species identity, age, sex and the reproductive status of a female.

Female wolf spiders *Schizocosa ocreata* rarely mate with more than one male and, once they have mated, are more likely to cannibalise (eat) males. Males, on the other hand, will often try to mate with more than one female.

The male has a courtship behaviour called a "jerky tap" that elicits a reaction from the female. The Table below shows measurements of the time taken for males to produce the jerky tap response after exposure to samples of silks from different origins.

Origin of silk	*Time until jerky tap response* (s)
Subadult female	155
Unmated adult female	22
Mated adult female	105

(a) (i) State **one** conclusion that can be drawn from these results.

1

(ii) What name is given to the delay between stimulus and response?

1

(iii) Name another aspect of this jerky tap response that could be observed and used for comparison.

1

(iv) Suggest **one** disadvantage of laboratory-based research into animal behaviour.

1

(b) The "selfish gene" concept maintains that individual organisms should behave so as to maximise the survival of copies of their genes.

Give **one** reason why the genes responsible for a male spider's response to silk in the selection of a mate can be described as "selfish".

1

(5)

Marks

ANIMAL BEHAVIOUR (continued)

3. Cheetahs (*Acinonyx jubatus*) in the Serengeti National Park in Tanzania kill more male Thomson's gazelles (*Gazella thomsoni*) than would be expected from the sex ratio of the local gazelle population.

The Table below shows data obtained by observing groups of Thomson's gazelles.

	males	*females*
Proportion on periphery of group (%)	75	53
Nearest neighbour distance (m)	9·3	4·6
Proportion of time spent scanning with head up (%)	8·4	11·4
Proportion in population (%)	30	70
Proportion hunted (%)	63	37

(a) Suggest why male Thomson's gazelles are more likely than females to be selected as prey by hunting cheetahs.   **1**

(b) Calculate the number of males on the periphery of a group of 80 gazelles.   **1**

(c) What name is given to the scanning behaviour?   **1**

                                                                        (3)

4. Describe how appeasement and ritualised displays in agonistic interactions can benefit all members of social groups. Illustrate your answer by reference to named species.   **(5)**

                                                                        (20)

[End of *Animal Behaviour* questions. *Physiology, Health and Exercise* questions start on Page 24]

[Turn over

SECTION C (continued) *Marks*

PHYSIOLOGY, HEALTH AND EXERCISE

1. (a) The graph shows obesity data for England in 1993 and 2002.

   Individuals were described as obese if they had a body mass index (BMI) of 30 or greater.

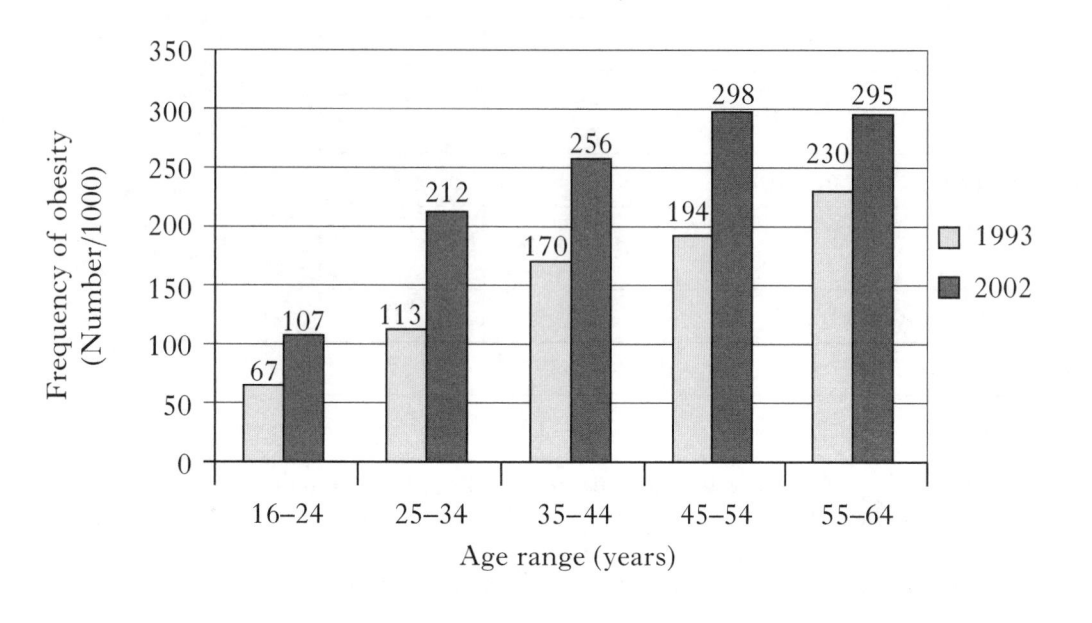

   (i) What two measurements are needed to calculate BMI? **1**

   (ii) Obesity has increased in all age ranges over the ten year period.

   Which age range has shown the biggest percentage increase? **1**

   (iii) Give **one** other general trend shown by the data. **1**

   (iv) Name **one** medical condition for which obesity is a risk factor. **1**

   (b) (i) Bioelectrical impedance analysis (BIA) is a method used to determine percentage body fat. Outline the principle on which this method is based. **2**

   (ii) Give **one** limitation of BIA. **1**

   (7)

2. Discuss the changes that take place in the cardiovascular system during a short period of strenuous exercise. **(4)**

PHYSIOLOGY, HEALTH AND EXERCISE (continued)

Marks

3. The Bruce protocol is a method used in maximal exercise testing to determine fitness. A subject wearing an oxygen-monitoring mask is supervised running on a treadmill while the gradient (slope) and speed of the treadmill are both increased in a standard way. When the subject is exhausted, the time is noted.

   The Table below shows some results from a study using this method. The values have been selected for four young healthy males who each took the same time to reach exhaustion.

Time (min)	Body mass (kg)	Maximum oxygen uptake ($l\,min^{-1}$)	Fitness ($ml\,kg^{-1}\,min^{-1}$)
10·5	70	2·53	36·2
10·5	75	2·72	36·2
10·5	85	3·08	36·2
10·5	90	3·26	36·2

   (a) Explain why measuring oxygen uptake is a valid way to assess fitness.

   2

   (b) Explain why the "Fitness" measurement is independent of body mass.

   1

   (c) Calculate the maximum oxygen uptake of an 80 kg male who took 10·5 minutes to reach exhaustion in the same test.

   1

   (d) Give an example of a situation where the individual given a treadmill test would **not** be stressed to exhaustion.

   1

   (5)

[**Turn over for Question 4 on** *Page twenty-six*

PHYSIOLOGY, HEALTH AND EXERCISE (continued)   *Marks*

4. In an investigation into energy expenditure measured by direct calorimetry, subjects at rest were given a solution of either glucose or sucrose (a disaccharide). The results are shown in the graph below.

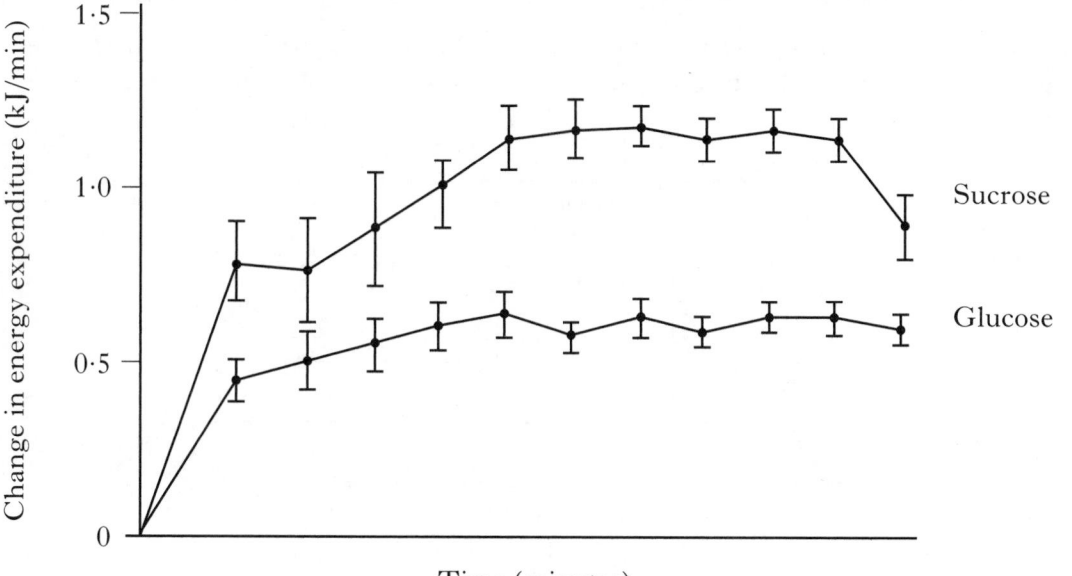

(a) Which component of total energy expenditure is being investigated in this study?   **1**

(b) What evidence is there that diet affects energy expenditure?   **1**

(c) What do the error bars in the graph indicate about the results presented?   **1**

(d) The results in this investigation were obtained by direct calorimetry.

Give **one** way in which indirect calorimetry differs from direct calorimetry.   **1**

(4)

(20)

[END OF QUESTION PAPER]

ADVANCED HIGHER

2010

[BLANK PAGE]

X007/701

NATIONAL
QUALIFICATIONS
2010

THURSDAY, 27 MAY
1.00 PM – 3.30 PM

BIOLOGY
ADVANCED HIGHER

SECTION A—Questions 1–25 (25 marks)

Instructions for completion of Section A are given on *Page two*.

SECTIONS B AND C

The answer to each question should be written in ink in the answer book provided. Any additional paper (if used) should be placed inside the front cover of the answer book.

Rough work should be scored through.

Section B (55 marks)

All questions should be attempted. Candidates should note that Question 8 contains a choice.

Question 1 is on Pages 10, 11 and 12. Questions 2 and 3 are on Page 13. Pages 12 and 13 are fold-out pages.

Section C (20 marks)

Candidates should attempt the questions in **one** unit, **either** Biotechnology **or** Animal Behaviour **or** Physiology, Health and Exercise.

Read carefully

1   Check that the answer sheet provided is for **Biology Advanced Higher (Section A)**.

2   For this section of the examination you must use an **HB pencil** and, where necessary, an eraser.

3   Check that the answer sheet you have been given has **your name**, **date of birth**, **SCN** (Scottish Candidate Number) and **Centre Name** printed on it.

     Do not change any of these details.

4   If any of this information is wrong, tell the Invigilator immediately.

5   If this information is correct, **print** your name and seat number in the boxes provided.

6   The answer to each question is **either** A, B, C or D. Decide what your answer is, then, using your pencil, put a horizontal line in the space provided (see sample question below).

7   There is **only one correct** answer to each question.

8   Any rough working should be done on the question paper or the rough working sheet, **not** on your answer sheet.

9   At the end of the examination, put the **answer sheet for Section A inside the front cover of the answer book**.

Sample Question

Which of the following molecules contains six carbon atoms?

A   Glucose

B   Pyruvic acid

C   Ribulose bisphosphate

D   Acetyl coenzyme A

The correct answer is **A**—Glucose. The answer **A** has been clearly marked in **pencil** with a horizontal line (see below).

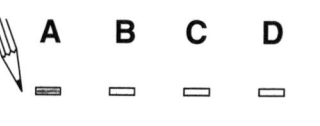

Changing an answer

If you decide to change your answer, carefully erase your first answer and using your pencil, fill in the answer you want. The answer below has been changed to **D**.

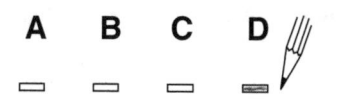

SECTION A

All questions in this section should be attempted.

Answers should be given on the separate answer sheet provided.

1. The following diagram represents a bacterial cell.

Which **one** of the following correctly identifies the structures labelled 1, 2 and 3?

	1	2	3
A	plasmid	flagellum	capsule
B	flagellum	capsule	plasmid
C	plasmid	capsule	flagellum
D	capsule	plasmid	flagellum

2. Plasmodesmata are structures that link

   A   cell walls in adjacent prokaryotic cells

   B   cell walls in adjacent eukaryotic cells

   C   cell cytoplasm in adjacent prokaryotic cells

   D   cell cytoplasm in adjacent eukaryotic cells.

3. The key below shows features of biological molecules.

   1   Soluble in water......................go to 2
        Insoluble in water..................go to 3

   2   Extracellular...........................A
        Hydrolytic.............................B

   3   Storage.................................C
        Structural.............................D

   Which letter could be both triglycerides and glycogen?

4. The diagram below shows the changes in cell mass and DNA mass during two cell cycles.

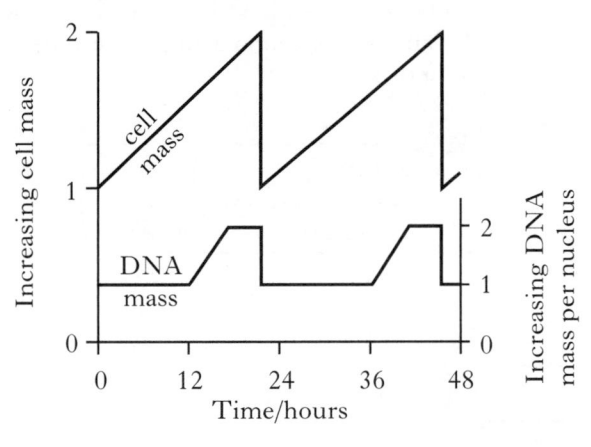

What valid conclusion could be made from the graph?

During the cell cycle

   A   interphase is the longest phase

   B   mitosis is divided into four phases

   C   replication takes place between 0 and 12 hours

   D   cytokinesis takes place at 12 and 36 hours.

5. Which line in the table below correctly describes adenine and thymine and the bonding between them in a DNA molecule?

	Adenine	*Number of hydrogen bonds*	*Thymine*
A	purine	two	pyrimidine
B	pyrimidine	three	purine
C	pyrimidine	two	purine
D	purine	three	pyrimidine

[Turn over

6. One cause of cystic fibrosis is a mutation in the CFTR gene which codes for 1480 amino acids. The most common mutation results in the deletion of one amino acid.

Which line in the table below shows correctly the number of nucleotides in the mutated gene and the number of amino acids in the protein that is synthesised?

	Number of nucleotides encoding the mutated gene	Number of amino acids in the protein synthesised
A	4431	1477
B	4439	1480
C	4437	1479
D	4439	1479

7. The diagram below shows the distribution of protein molecules in a cell membrane.

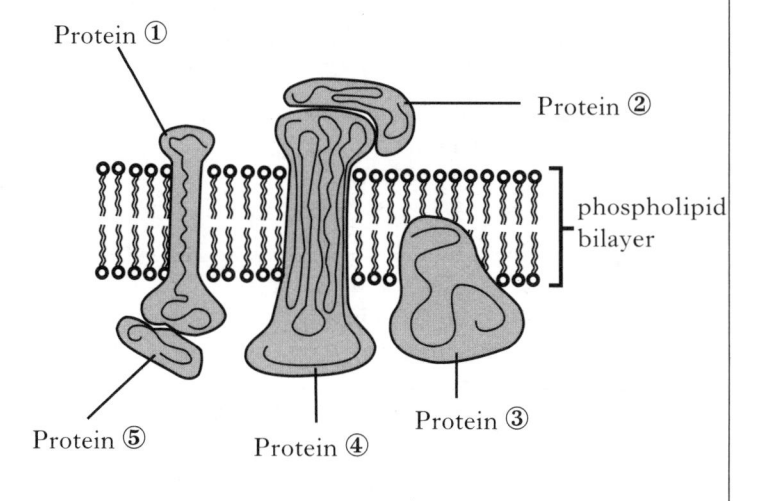

Protein ①

Protein ②

phospholipid bilayer

Protein ⑤

Protein ④

Protein ③

Which line in the table below correctly identifies a peripheral and an integral membrane protein?

	Peripheral membrane protein	Integral membrane protein
A	1	5
B	2	1
C	3	4
D	5	2

8. The diagram below shows a metabolic pathway that is controlled by end product inhibition.

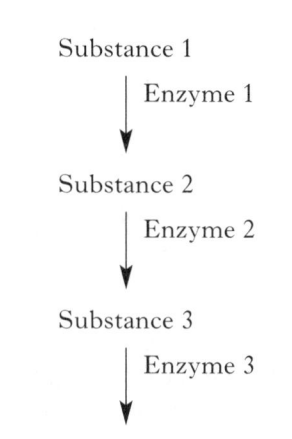

Substance 1

Enzyme 1

Substance 2

Enzyme 2

Substance 3

Enzyme 3

Substance 4

For Substance 4 to bring about end product inhibition, which of the following will it interact with?

A   Substance 1

B   Substance 3

C   Enzyme 1

D   Enzyme 3

9. Covalent modification of enzymes is used to control their activity.

Which of the following processes involves the covalent modification of an enzyme?

A   The conversion of trypsinogen into trypsin.

B   The end-product inhibition of phosphatase.

C   The allosteric inhibition of glycogen phosphorylase.

D   The conversion of sucrose into glucose and fructose.

10. Which of the following acts as a hydrophobic extracellular signalling molecule?

A   Insulin

B   Testosterone

C   Acetylcholine

D   Cholesterol

11. The following stages are involved in amplifying DNA fragments using the polymerase chain reaction (PCR).

    V   DNA denatures

    W   Primers bind

    X   Complementary DNA strands replicated

    Y   Temperature changed to about 75 °C

    Z   Temperature changed to about 55 °C

    After heating the fragments to about 95 °C, which of the following sequences occurs?

    A   X, Z, V, Y, W

    B   Z, V, W, Y, X

    C   V, X, Z, W, Y

    D   V, Z, W, Y, X

12. A piece of DNA 20 kilobase pairs (kbp) long was digested using different restriction enzymes. BamHI, EcoRI and PstI. The results are shown in the table below.

	Restriction enzyme used			
	PstI	BamHI	EcoRI	BamHI PstI
Lengths of DNA fragments (kbp)	15	17	12	12
	5	3	8	5
				3

    Which of the following set of fragments would result if all three enzymes were used together?

    A   7, 5, 3, 2

    B   8, 7, 3, 2

    C   12, 3, 2

    D   9, 5, 3, 3

13. A certain restriction enzyme will only cut a DNA strand between two Cs when the base sequence CCGG is present.

    Two homologous segments of DNA that carry different alleles of a gene are shown below. Allele 2 has a single base-pair difference.

    Allele 1 was treated with the restriction enzyme and the fragments *w*, *x* and *y* were obtained and separated by gel electrophoresis. The resulting band pattern for allele 1 is shown below.

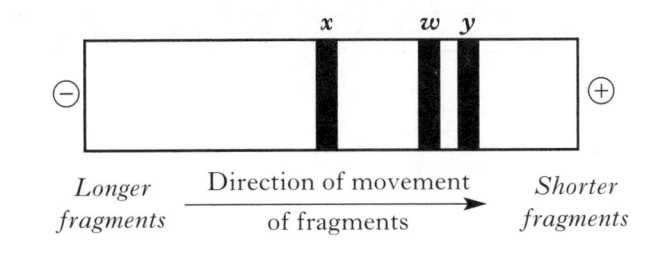

    Which of the following band patterns would result when the procedure was repeated using allele 2?

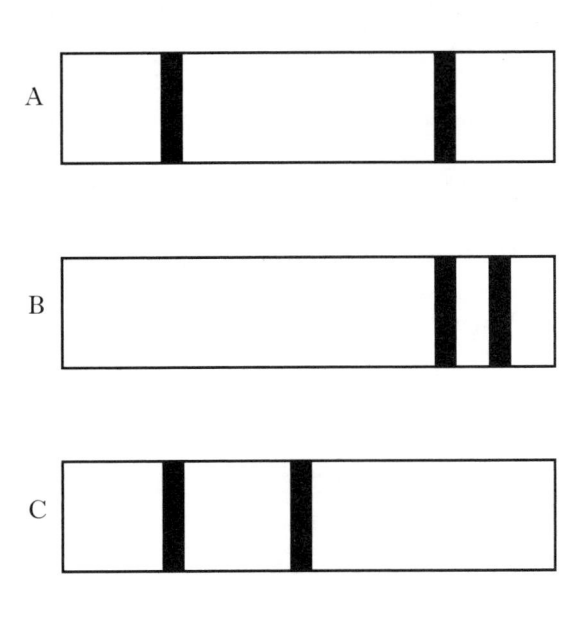

14. Several species of bacteria have been found deep under the Pacific Ocean, where hot water escapes from the sea bed.

In these marine ecosystems, the bacteria can use hydrogen sulphide as an energy source to fix carbon dioxide into organic molecules. When the bacteria break down, organic material is released, which filter feeders consume.

This information indicates that the bacteria are

A   heterotrophs

B   detritivores

C   autotrophs

D   decomposers.

15. Three pyramids of numbers are shown below.

Which of the following food chains **cannot** be represented by any of these pyramids?

A   Oak tree → leaf miner → tree warbler

B   Algae → pond snail → nematode parasite

C   Grass plants → rabbit → stoat

D   Phytoplankton → zooplankton → herring

16. The table below shows data obtained from an investigation into the mass and population density of some organisms in a heathland food web.

Which line in the table shows correctly the species with the highest biomass per square metre?

	Species	Mean mass of organism (g)	Population density (numbers m^{-2})
A	cricket	0·10	4
B	ladybird	0·03	20
C	aphid	0·002	5420
D	weevil	0·005	3250

17. The diagram below shows the nitrogen cycle.

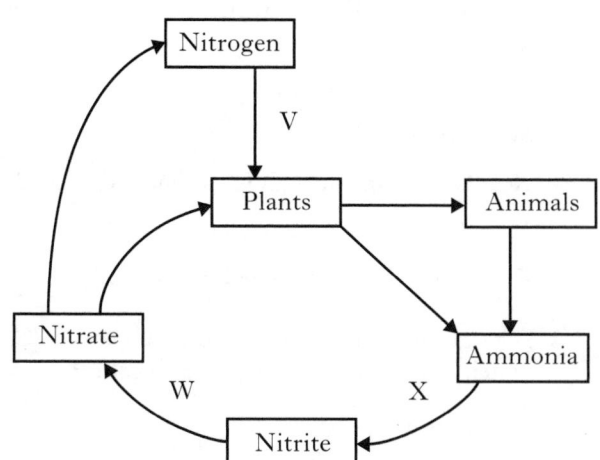

Which line in the table below correctly identifies the micro-organisms involved at the stages shown?

	V	W	X
A	*Nitrosomonas*	*Nitrobacter*	*Rhizobium*
B	*Rhizobium*	*Nitrobacter*	*Nitrosomonas*
C	*Nitrobacter*	*Rhizobium*	*Nitrosomonas*
D	*Rhizobium*	*Nitrosomonas*	*Nitrobacter*

18. The table below shows four examples of interactions between species.

Which column in the table shows correctly the benefits (+) or costs (−) which result from each interaction?

Interaction	A	B	C	D
Sheep grazing in a field of grass	+/−	+/−	+/+	+/−
Owls and foxes hunting for the same food	+/−	−/−	−/−	+/−
Corals acting as hosts for zooxanthellae	+/−	+/+	+/+	+/+
"Cleaner fish" feeding on parasites which they remove from other fish	+/+	+/+	+/−	+/+

19. Anolis lizards are found on Caribbean islands. They feed on prey of various sizes.

Histogram 1 shows the range of prey length eaten by *Anolis marmoratus* on the island of Jarabacoa, where there are five other Anolis species.

Histogram 2 shows the range of prey length eaten by *Anolis marmoratus* on the island of Marie Galante, where it is the only Anolis species.

Histogram 1: Jarabacoa Island

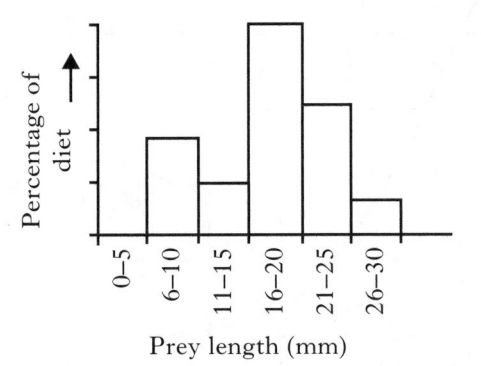

Prey length (mm)

Histogram 2: Marie Galante Island

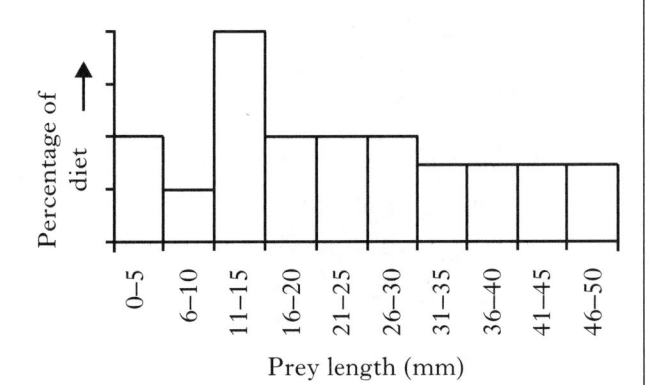

Prey length (mm)

Which of the following statements could explain the different range of prey sizes eaten by *Anolis marmoratus* on the two islands?

A   Larger numbers of prey are found on Marie Galante.

B   *Anolis marmoratus* occupies its fundamental niche on Jarabacoa.

C   *Anolis marmoratus* occupies its realised niche on Marie Galante.

D   Resource partitioning takes place on Jarabacoa.

20. Each statement below applies to either conformation or regulation.

1   A wide range of habitats can be occupied
2   A restricted range of habitats can be occupied
3   There is a high energy cost
4   There is no energy cost

Which statements apply to conformation?

A   1 and 4

B   1 and 3

C   2 and 4

D   2 and 3

21. The figure below shows the general relationships between the internal environment and variation in the external environment of four animals.

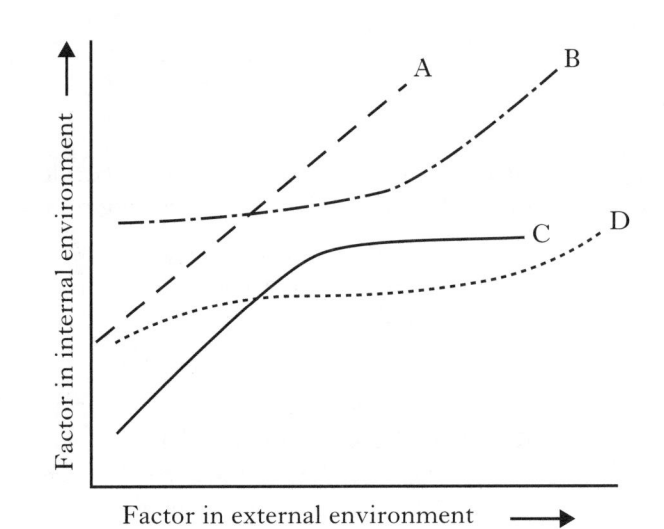

Which animal is the most effective regulator?

[Turn over

22. Eutrophication can result from agricultural activity.

Which of the following defines eutrophication?

A   Algal bloom

B   Increased BOD

C   Loss of diversity

D   Nutrient enrichment

23. The figure below represents part of an aquatic food web.

P1 and P2 are producers.

C1, C2 and C3 are consumers.

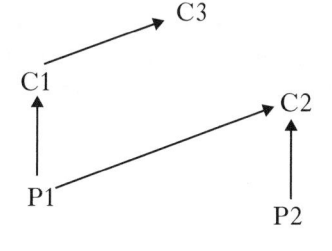

Analysis of a persistent organic pesticide in this ecosystem produced the following results:

Result 1   P1 has a higher concentration of the pesticide in its tissues than is present in the surrounding water.

Result 2   C2 converts the pesticide into a more toxic chemical in its tissues.

Result 3   The concentration of the pesticide in P1 is lower than that in C1 which, in turn, is lower than that in C3.

Which row in the table shows the processes responsible for Results 1, 2 and 3?

	Result 1	Result 2	Result 3
A	bioaccumulation	biotransformation	biomagnification
B	biomagnification	biotransformation	bioaccumulation
C	biotransformation	bioaccumulation	biomagnification
D	bioaccumulation	biomagnification	biotransformation

24. The insecticide DDT is metabolised in birds to DDE. The level of DDE in eggs affects the shell thickness. Premature egg breakage begins when mean shell thickness is 80% of normal.

The graph below shows how DDE content of the diet affects DDE content of eggs and mean shell thickness.

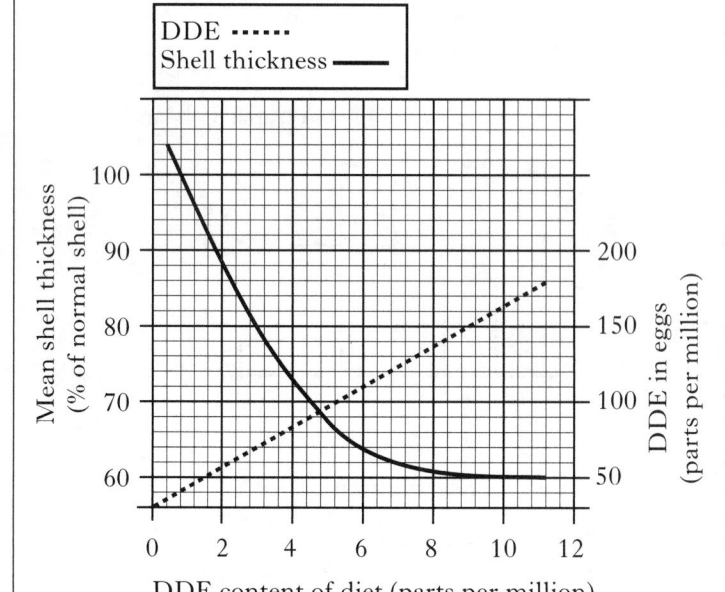

What would be the minimum DDE concentration to cause the start of premature egg breakage?

A   150 parts per million

B   70 parts per million

C   9 parts per million

D   3 parts per million

25. Succession which follows the clearing of long-established farm land is described as

A   allogenic

B   secondary

C   degradative

D   primary.

[END OF SECTION A]

Candidates are reminded that the answer sheet MUST be returned INSIDE the front cover of the answer book.

[Turn over for Section B on Page ten

SECTION B

All questions in this section should be attempted.
All answers must be written clearly and legibly in ink.

1. Proto-oncogenes code for proteins that stimulate cell division. When these genes mutate they can become oncogenes and cause the excessive cell proliferation associated with tumour formation.

   A recent study investigated a chromosome mutation discovered in lung tumour cells. The mutation is a rearrangement of two genes on the same chromosome, resulting in the fusion of the two genes (Figure 1). The genes are *EML4*, which is involved in microtubule formation, and *ALK* which codes for a kinase enzyme. As a result of this fusion, a new protein is formed that has uncontrolled kinase activity inside the cell.

   Figure 1 : Formation of the EML4–ALK fusion gene

   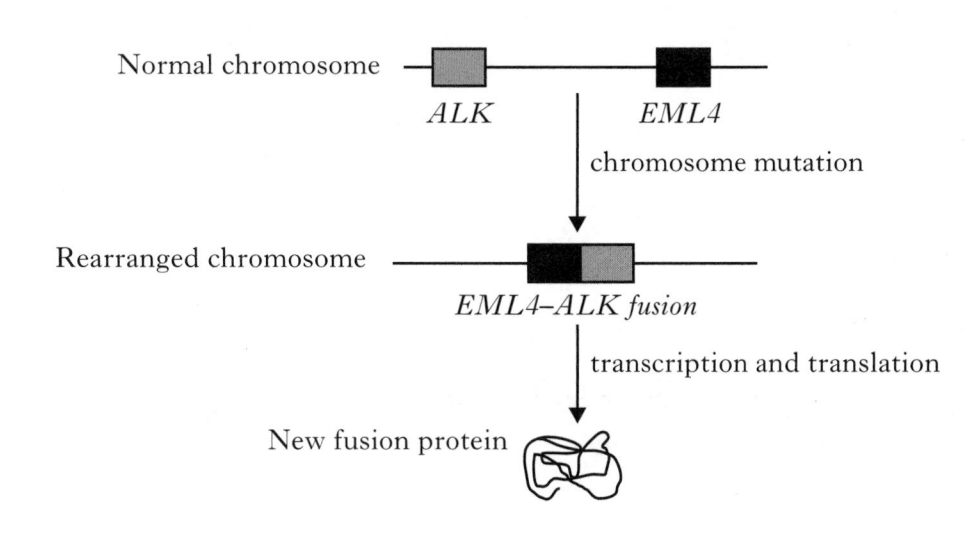

   Part of the study aimed to find out if normal cells are transformed to divide abnormally after treatment with the fusion gene. In the treatments, genes were introduced into normal cells that were then cultured in a flat dish containing a suitable growth medium. Abnormal cell division is indicated by the transformed cells stacking up in multiple layers called *foci*.

   The four gene treatments used are shown in the Table. In the fourth, the *EML4–ALK* fusion gene was modified so that the kinase produced was inactive.

   Table: Results of cell transformation study

Gene treatment	Formation of foci
ALK alone	no
EML4 alone	no
EML4–ALK fusion	yes
EML4–ALK fusion modified	no

Question 1 (continued)

The study also investigated the possibility that kinase inhibitors could be used to treat tumours arising from the fusion gene. The growth of normal and transformed cells suspended in liquid culture was monitored in the presence and absence of a kinase inhibitor. The results are shown in Figures 2 and 3.

Figure 2: Effect of kinase inhibitor on normal cells

KEY

● 0 μmol 1^{-1}

○ 5 μmol 1^{-1}

□ 10 μmol 1^{-1}

Figure 3: Effect of kinase inhibitor on cells transformed with *EML4–ALK*

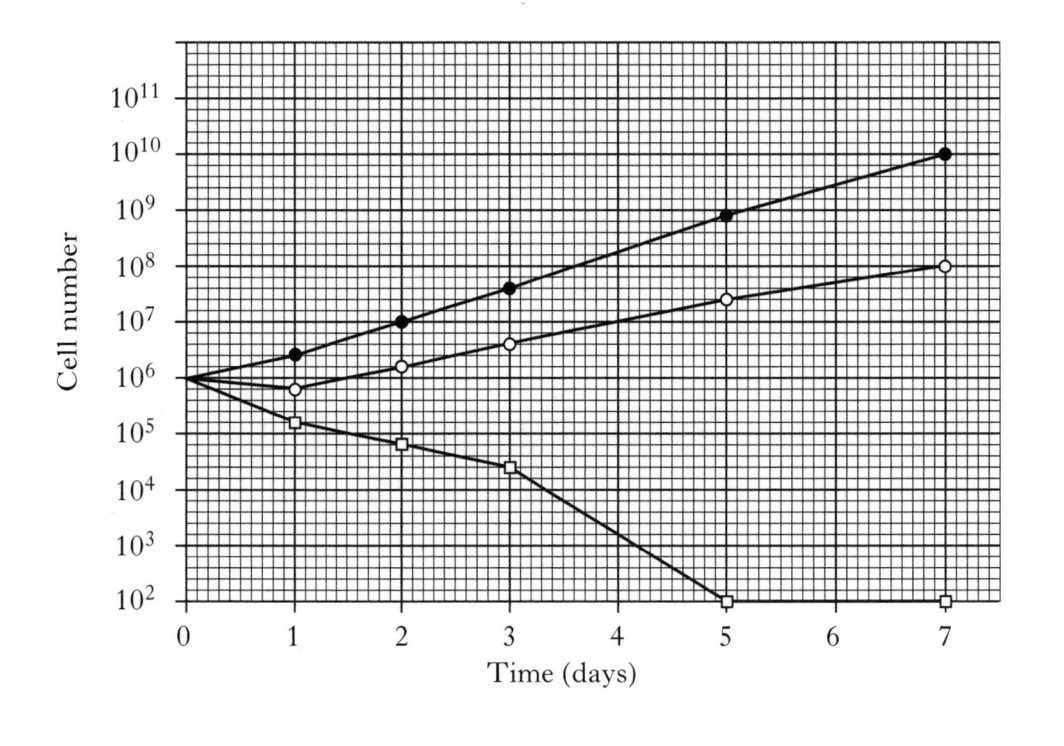

[Question 1 continues on *Page twelve*

Marks

Question 1 (continued)

(a) State why abnormal proliferation of cells can occur when only one copy of an oncogene is present.

1

(b) (i) In the study, abnormal cells formed *foci*. Describe the appearance of a culture of normal animal cells that have stopped dividing.

2

(ii) Give a reason for adding fetal bovine serum to cell culture medium.

1

(c) Refer to the table. Explain how the results show that:

(i) the chromosome rearrangement created an oncogene;

1

(ii) the effect of the fusion gene is uncontrolled kinase activity.

2

(d) Use data from Figures 2 and 3 to show that normal and transformed cells are capable of dividing at the same rate.

1

(e) Refer to Figures 2 and 3.

(i) Show that the $10 \, \mu mol \, l^{-1}$ inhibitor concentration reduces the proliferation of normal cells by a factor of 100.

1

(ii) What general trend is observed for the growth of cells when the concentration of inhibitor is varied?

1

(iii) Use data from the $5 \, \mu mol \, l^{-1}$ concentration to show that transformed cells are more sensitive to the presence of the inhibitor than normal cells.

1

(f) The study aimed to find a possible therapy for tumours caused by fusion mutation. How do the results suggest that $10 \, \mu mol \, l^{-1}$ of inhibitor would be the most useful to test on patients?

2

(13)

[Questions 2 and 3 are on fold-out *Page thirteen*

Marks

2. The cell wall of the prokaryote *E. coli* is made of a substance that consists of polysaccharide chains cross-linked by short chains of amino acids. The polysaccharide is made up of two kinds of sugar: N-acetylmuramate (NAM) and N-acetylglucosamine (NAG). NAM and NAG alternate along the chain and differ from glucose only at the C2 and C3 positions.

(a) Name the substance that makes up the cell wall of *E. coli*.   1

(b) NAM and NAG are joined by a glycosidic bond.

   (i) Explain why this bond is described as $\beta(1-4)$.   2

   (ii) The enzyme lysozyme damages bacterial cell walls by breaking the bonds between NAM and NAG.

      What type of reaction is catalysed by lysozyme?   1

                                                              (4)

3. Describe the transport of sodium and potassium ions across the plasma membrane.   (5)

Marks

4. Transgenic plants can be produced using genetically engineered plasmids. The plasmids are obtained from bacteria that naturally infect plant cells. A modified plasmid is shown in the diagram below.

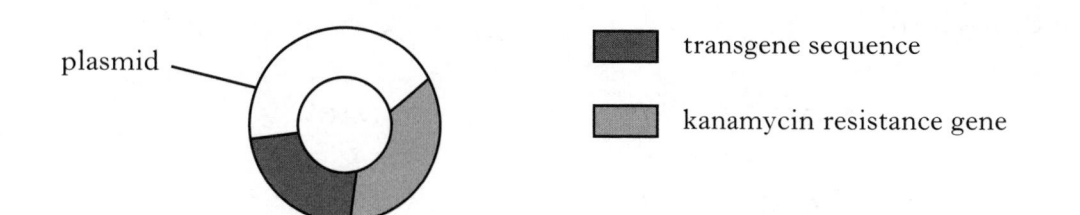

plasmid

■ transgene sequence

▨ kanamycin resistance gene

Bacterial cells containing the modified plasmid are incubated with plant cells. The plant cells are then cultured in a growth medium containing kanamycin.

(a) What is meant by the term transgenic?　　　　　　　　　　　　　1

(b) Name the bacterial source of these plasmids.　　　　　　　　　　1

(c) Explain the role of kanamycin in the production of transgenic plants.　2

(d) Give **one** example of the use of this transgenic technology.　　　1

(5)

Marks

5.　Bramble plants (*Rubus fruticosus*) are pollinated by a variety of nectar-feeding insects, such as the meadow brown butterfly (*Maniola jurtina*). Bramble flowers are one of many nectar sources for this species.

A study focused on competitive interactions occurring between meadow browns and other insects at bramble flowers. The average time a meadow brown spent feeding when not disturbed by another insect is shown in the bar graph at A. The other bars show its feeding duration when another insect was also present.

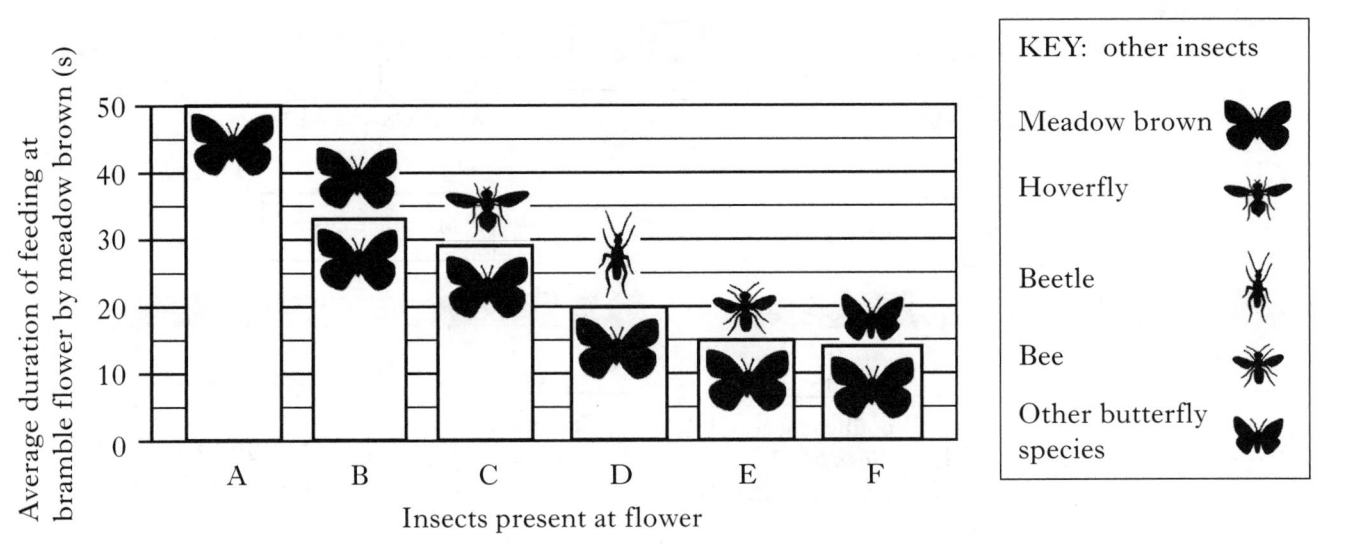

(a)　Explain why intraspecific competition is expected to be more intense than interspecific.　1

(b)　(i)　Which bar represents intraspecific competition?　1

　　　(ii)　Give **one** general conclusion that can be drawn from these data about competitive interactions at bramble flowers?　1

(c)　From the information provided, state why the relationship between meadow brown butterflies and bramble plants is not an example of mutualism even though there are benefits to both species.　1

(4)

[Turn over

Marks

6. A laboratory experiment investigated the decomposition of beech (*Fagus sylvatica*) leaves following four different treatments. Fresh leaves were either left to form leaf litter or were fed to herbivorous caterpillars to form caterpillar faeces. The mass losses of these samples were then compared with and without the detritivore activity of woodlice.

Figure 1 shows the four treatments carried out. Figure 2 shows the mass loss of the four samples produced over a twelve week period.

Figure 1

Figure 2

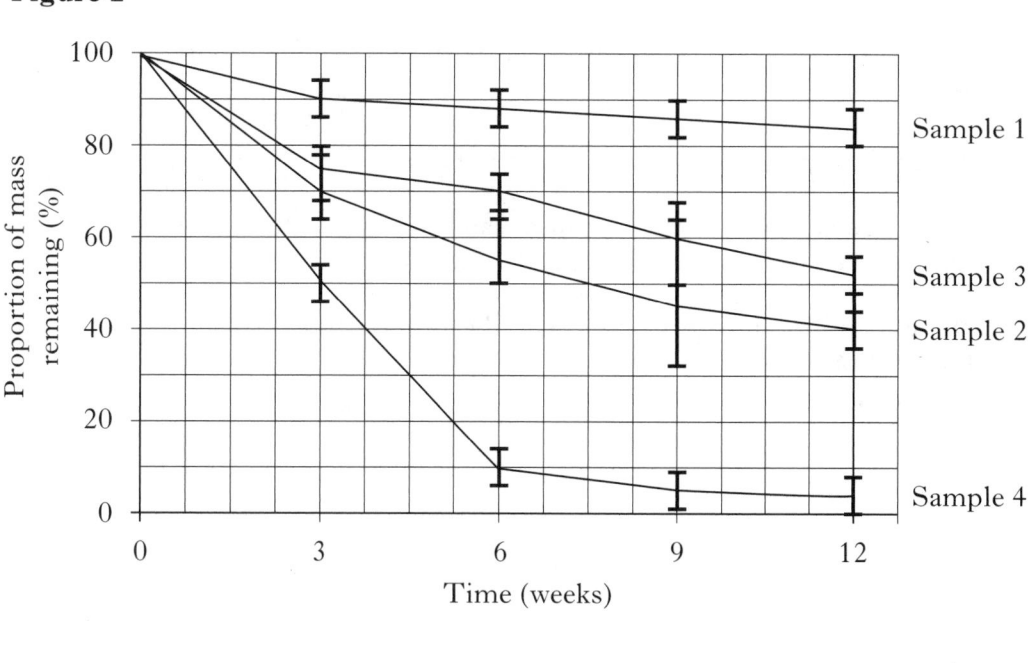

(a) How do the diets of herbivores and detritivores differ?   1

(b) Refer to Figure 2.

   (i) What evidence is there that leaves passing through the guts of two invertebrates decompose more than seven times faster than leaves allowed to form leaf litter?   2

   (ii) Use the error bars to comment on the results obtained for Samples 2 and 3 after 9 weeks.   1

   (iii) Explain why Sample 4 shows the most rapid loss in mass.   1

(5)

Marks

7. (a) Explain how the level of pollution in an ecosystem could be monitored using changes in population.   **2**

   (b) The widespread use of the drug diclofenac to treat cattle in the Indian subcontinent has led to a rapid decline in the populations of various species of vulture. For example, in 2008 the population of the oriental white-backed vulture (*Gyps bengalensis*) was estimated to be 11 000, a decline of 99·9% since 1992. Although diclofenac has low persistence and generally it has low toxicity, vultures are now known to be unusually susceptible to it.

   (i) What was the population of *Gyps bengalensis* in 1992?   **1**

   (ii) Explain why the effect on the vulture populations is greatest when they feed on carcasses of cattle treated with diclofenac shortly before their death.   **1**

   (4)

8. Answer **either** A **or** B.

   A. Increasing the rate of food production to meet global demands is challenging.

   Discuss the management of the environment for intensive food production with reference to:

   (i) control of species that reduce yield;   **7**

   (ii) monoculture.   **8**

   (15)

   OR

   B. Plants are increasingly being cultivated for biomass as an alternative source of energy to fossil fuels.

   Discuss:

   (i) energy fixation and primary productivity;   **5**

   (ii) fossil fuels and air pollution.   **10**

   (15)

[END OF SECTION B]

[Turn over

SECTION C

Candidates should attempt questions on <u>one</u> unit, <u>either</u> Biotechnology <u>or</u> Animal Behaviour <u>or</u> Physiology, Health and Exercise.

The questions on Biotechnology can be found on pages 18–20.

The questions on Animal Behaviour can be found on pages 22–25.

The questions on Physiology, Health and Exercise can be found on pages 26–28.

All answers must be written clearly and legibly in ink.

Labelled diagrams may be used where appropriate.

BIOTECHNOLOGY   *Marks*

1.   (a)   Legumes interact with bacteria to produce nitrogenase.

        (i)   Name the genes responsible for the synthesis of nitrogenase.   **1**

        (ii)   What chemical transformation is catalysed by nitrogenase?   **1**

  (b)   Sea buckthorn (*Hippophae rhamnoides*) produces fruit that has potential as a food and medicinal crop. Although not a legume, it has a symbiotic relationship in which nitrogenase is synthesised and the plant receives nitrate. When it is grown as a crop, nitrogen fertiliser is required to produce a high yield of fruit.

      The Figure below shows the effect of daily nitrate fertiliser application on nitrogenase activity in sea buckthorn root nodules over a period of 30 days.

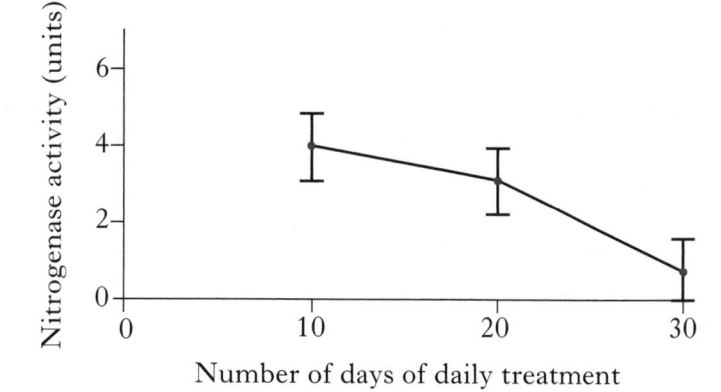

      Describe the effect of nitrate application on nitrogenase activity.   **2**

                                                          (4)

2.   Describe how B lymphocytes respond to foreign antigens. How is this response applied in the preparation of polyclonal sera?   **(5)**

Marks

BIOTECHNOLOGY (continued)

3. Bananas are important as a crop but the planting material required is often in short supply. Scientists have developed a micropropagation system as shown in the flow chart.

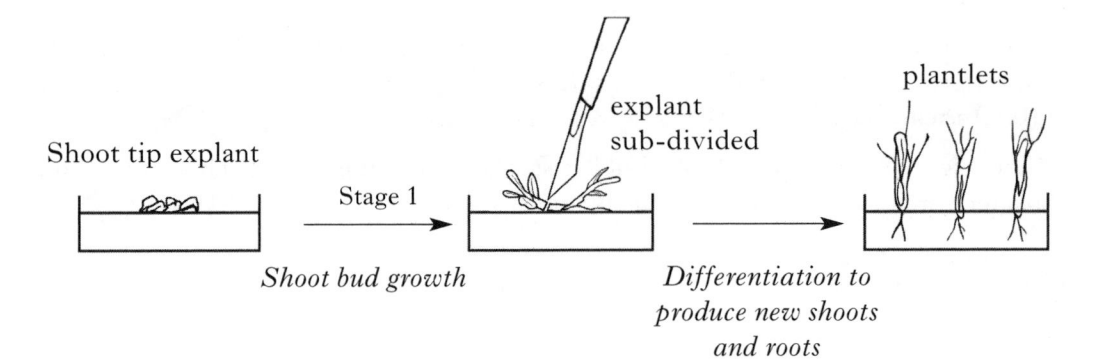

(a) Suggest **two** advantages of propagating banana plants using this system.   2

(b) State **two** environmental conditions that need to be controlled during the development of the plantlets.   1

(c) The effect of plant growth regulators on shoot regeneration in Stage 1 is shown in the table.

MS medium + growth regulators (mg l^{-1})		Explants differentiated (%)	Mean number of shoots per explant
+ IAA	+Kinetin		
0	0	29	2
0·1	1·0	42	4
0·1	2·5	46	8
0·1	5·0	58	8
0·5	1·0	54	12
0·5	2·5	66	20
0·5	5·0	58	28

(i) What evidence is there that growth regulators benefit propagation?   1

(ii) Use the data to explain why a growth regulator combination of 0·5 mg l^{-1} IAA + 5·0 mg l^{-1} kinetin is recommended.   1

(5)

[Turn over

Marks

BIOTECHNOLOGY (continued)

4. (a) Probiotics are produced by the dairy industry to provide health benefits beyond basic nutrition.

   Describe **one** such health benefit.   1

   (b) A company that produces a probiotic yoghurt drink claims there is a measurable beneficial effect when there are at least 10^{10} viable cells of *Lactobacillus casei* per $100 \, cm^3$ carton.

   The Figure shows how a biotechnologist used dilution plating to check the number of bacteria in a $100 \, cm^3$ carton of the drink.

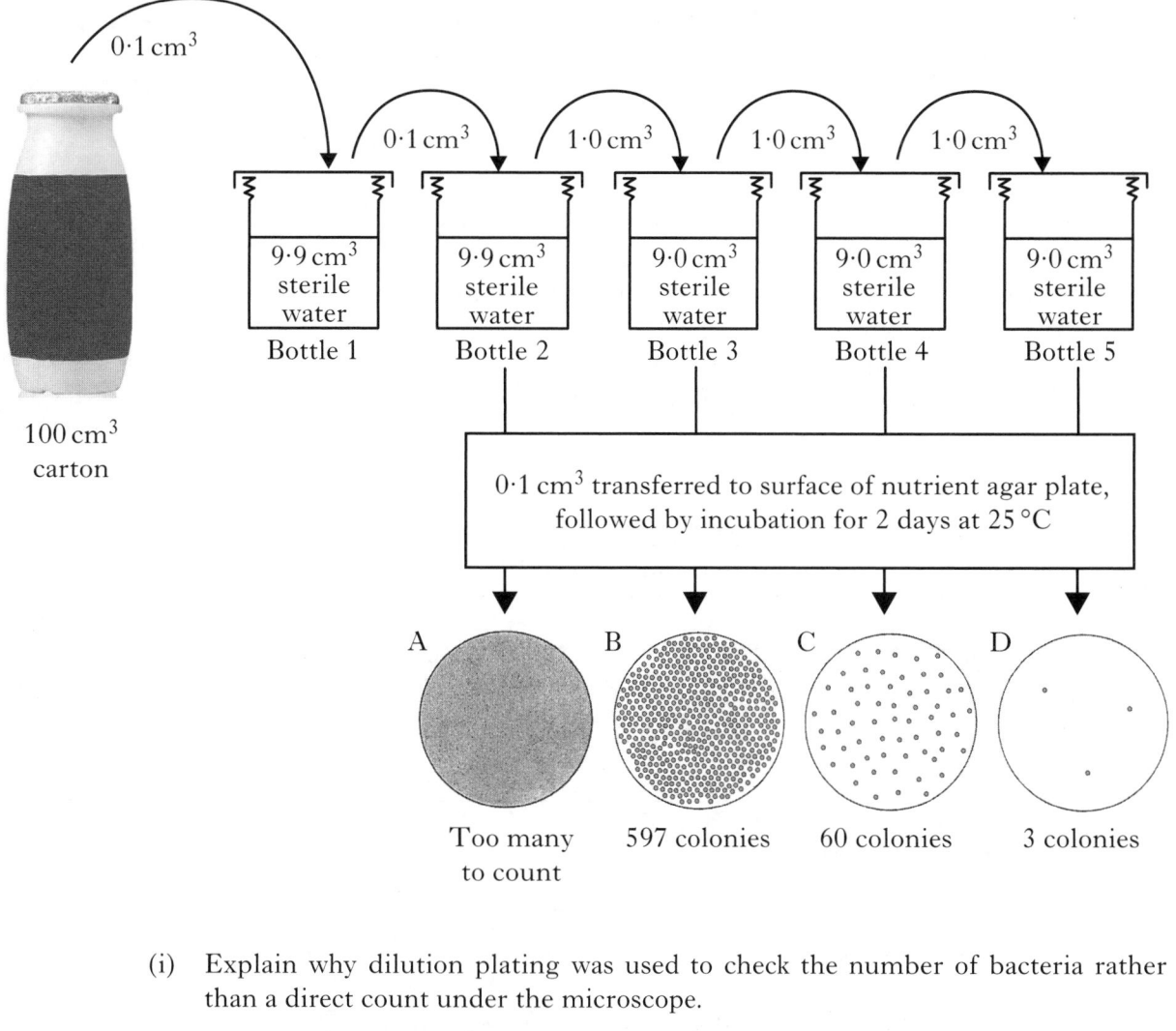

   (i) Explain why dilution plating was used to check the number of bacteria rather than a direct count under the microscope.   1

   (ii) Explain why sterile water was used throughout the dilution steps.   1

   (iii) Explain why plate C would be selected to check the number of bacteria in the drink.   1

   (iv) Use the information to show that more than 10^{10} viable cells were present in the carton.   2

   (6)

   (20)

[End of *Biotechnology* questions. *Animal Behaviour* questions start on Page 22]

[BLANK PAGE]

Marks

SECTION C (continued)

ANIMAL BEHAVIOUR

1. Many animals use colours and patterns to avoid predation. Some butterflies and moths, for example, have paired circular patterns on their wings.

   It has often been assumed that these wing spots are effective deterrents because they resemble the eyes of the predator's own enemies—the *eye mimicry hypothesis*. An alternative explanation suggests that the off-putting effect arises from visual contrast—the *conspicuous signal hypothesis*.

   In a recent experiment to test these hypotheses, targets made from triangular pieces of card were printed with the following patterns.

A	B	C
Uniform grey control	Two medium spots. Overall area equal to 3 spots in D	One large spot. Overall area equal to 3 spots in D
D	E	F
Three small spots	Two small spots	One small spot

   Each target had a mealworm attached to it. The targets were pinned to trees in woodland containing a variety of predatory bird species. They were checked for predation after 3, 24 and 48 hours. The survival of the mealworms indicated how successful the target patterns had been.

   (a) Suggest a variable that should be controlled in the placement of the targets.   1

   (b) With which target would there be least predation if the eye mimicry hypothesis is correct?   1

Marks

ANIMAL BEHAVIOUR (continued)

1. **(continued)**

    (c) The table below shows mealworm survival for each target following bird predation.

Target	Survival (%)		
	At 3 hours	At 24 hours	At 48 hours
A	65	8	2
B	95	45	21
C	97	48	20
D	93	35	12
E	88	30	8
F	90	25	6

    Explain how the results support the conspicuous signal hypothesis.   **2**

    (d) Name **one** other defence strategy where colour or pattern are used to avoid predation.   **1**

    (5)

2. Describe the benefits obtained by primates living in hierarchical groups.   **(4)**

[Turn over

Marks

ANIMAL BEHAVIOUR (continued)

3. Three-spined sticklebacks (*Gasterosteus aculeatus*) are fish widely distributed in rivers, lakes, ponds and estuaries throughout the British Isles. During the breeding season, from March to July, the male's throat and belly become a brilliant orange-red and his eyes electric-blue.

(a) In observations of breeding sticklebacks, a checklist of different actions may be used to help in the analysis of their behaviour.

What name is given to such a checklist?   1

(b) The breeding coloration of red throat and blue eye is found in male sticklebacks but not in females.

(i) What term is used to describe this difference between males and females?   1

(ii) State why the male's coloration is important in courtship.   1

(c) A wild, outbred population of sticklebacks was captured and inbred for two generations. The table below shows the effects of inbreeding on some aspects of reproduction in these sticklebacks.

Population	Fertilisation rate (%)	Hatching rate (%)
Wild/no inbreeding	98	94
One generation inbred	95	90
Two generations inbred	84	78

(i) Describe briefly how an inbred population could be produced.   1

(ii) How can these results be explained?   2

(6)

Marks

ANIMAL BEHAVIOUR (continued)

4. (*a*) The graphs below show survival of fruit flies (*Drosophila melanogaster*) from a normal-learning strain and a high-learning strain produced by artificial selection.

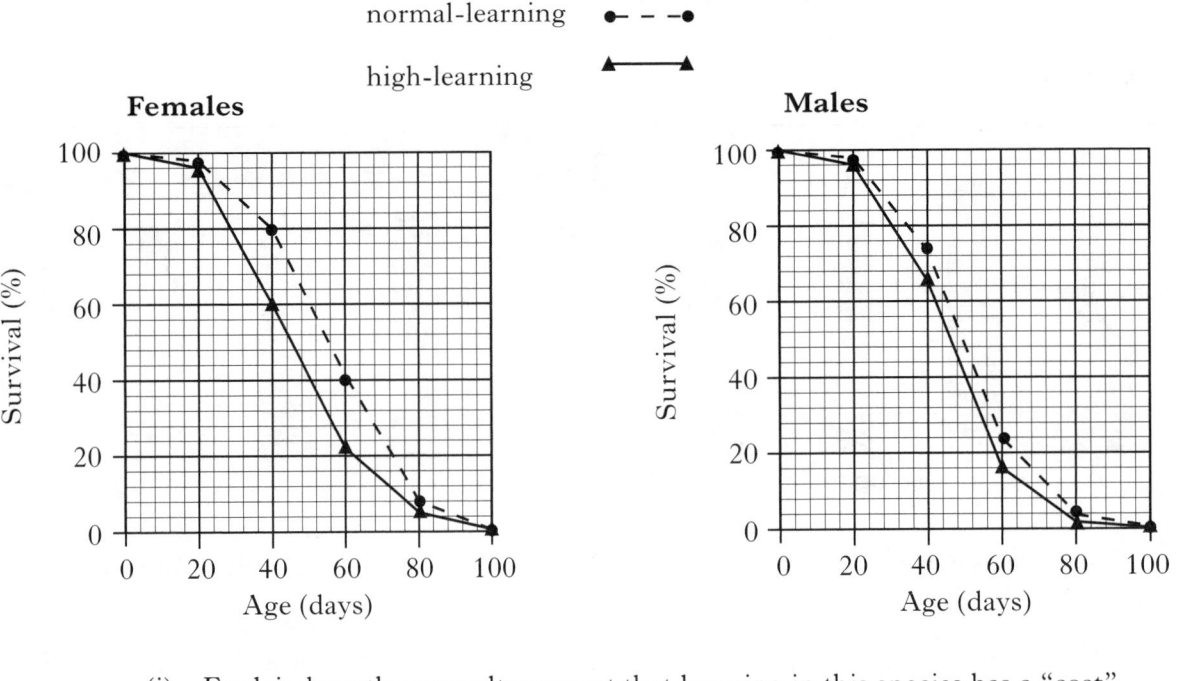

    (i) Explain how these results suggest that learning in this species has a "cost". **1**

    (ii) State **one** other conclusion that can be drawn from the results. **1**

    (iii) Why is such a cost unlikely to be observed in animals such as primates? **1**

(*b*) Describe **two** features of the learning process known as imprinting. **2**

(5)

(20)

[End of *Animal Behaviour* questions. *Physiology, Health and Exercise* questions start on Page 26]

[Turn over

Marks

SECTION C (continued)

PHYSIOLOGY, HEALTH AND EXERCISE

1. The Figures below show cardiac data for men between 18 and 34 years old who undertake different periods of sports training per week.

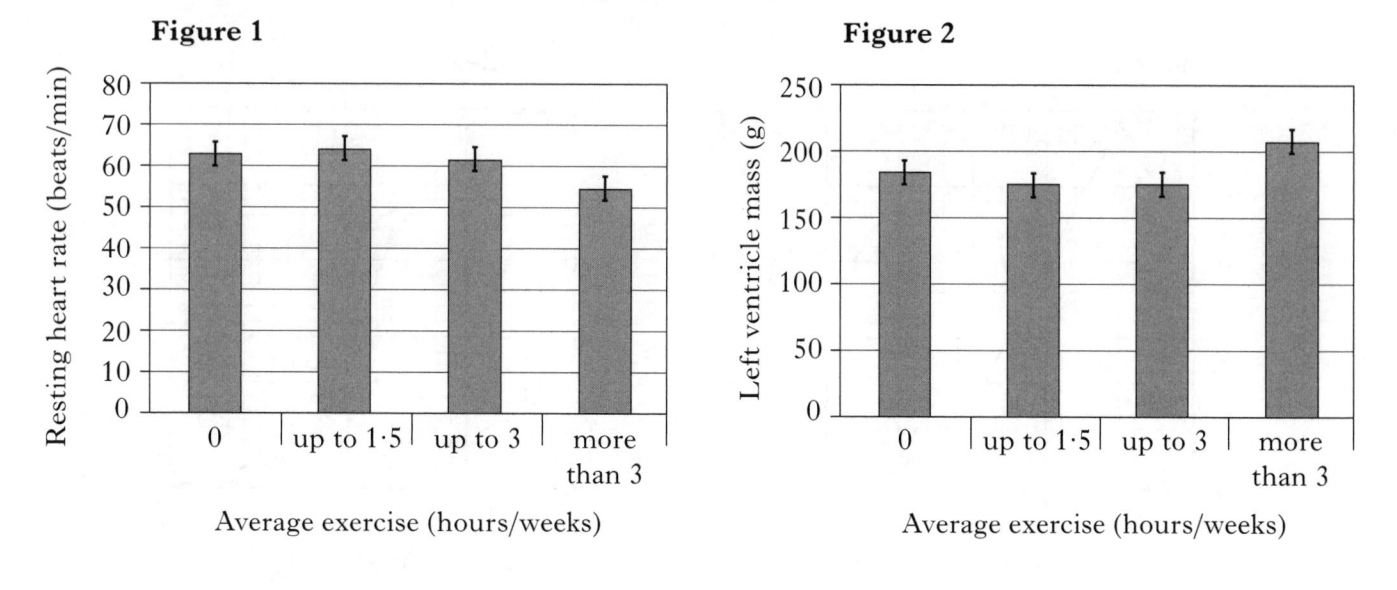

Figure 1

Figure 2

(a) Use information from both Figures to show that the "athletic heart" is an effect of prolonged training.   2

(b) What other information would be required to determine cardiac output?   1

(c) What is meant by the term *cardiac hypertrophy*?   1

(d) Give **one** example of a cardiovascular health benefit that could arise from exercising for less than three hours per week.   1

                                                                                  (5)

2. Describe the role of insulin in maintaining glucose balance and explain how non-insulin dependent diabetes mellitus (NIDDM) arises.   **(5)**

Marks

PHYSIOLOGY, HEALTH AND EXERCISE (continued)

3. The daily intake of calcium for different age groups of females was compared with the recommended intake level. The results shown in the Figure below indicate that actual intake exceeds the recommended level only up to the age of eight.

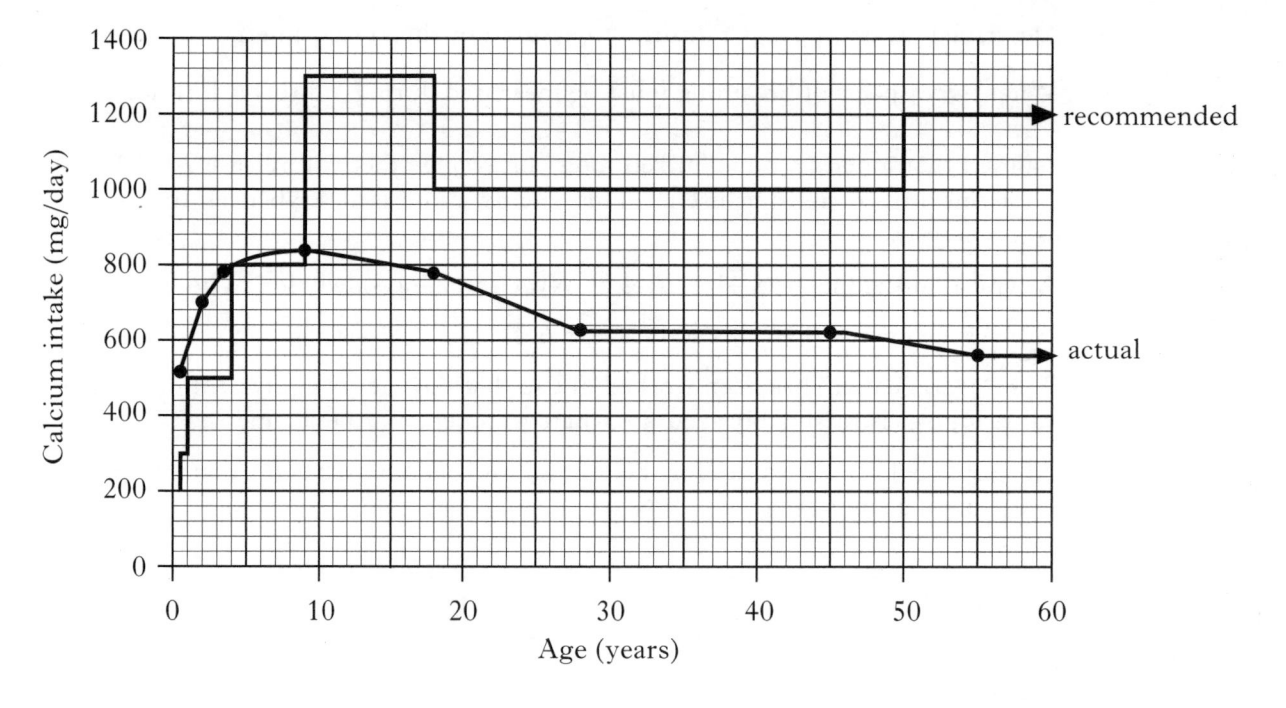

Explain why a high level of calcium intake is recommended for:

(a) the 9 to 18 age range;   1

(b) the over 50s.   2

(3)

[Turn over for Question 4 on *Page twenty-eight*

Marks

PHYSIOLOGY, HEALTH AND EXERCISE (continued)

4. (a) Direct calorimetry is an accurate but expensive way to measure human energy output.

    Indirect calorimetry uses measurements of oxygen consumption to estimate energy expenditure.

    (i) Describe how energy expenditure is measured by direct calorimetry.   2

    (ii) What **two** aspects of breathing must be measured during indirect calorimetry?   2

    (b) It is assumed that a person on a "mixed food" or average diet will release 20·20 kJ of energy for one litre of oxygen used. This energy value is described as the *energy equivalent of oxygen*.

    (i) A typical individual uses 41·5 litres of oxygen walking slowly for an hour.

    How much energy does this activity expend?   1

    (ii) The "average diet" has been worked out so that the energy equivalent of oxygen value it gives is reasonably accurate whatever a person's diet contains.

    The table below lists values for the energy equivalent of oxygen when the diet is made up of a single food.

Food	*Energy equivalent of oxygen* (kJ)
Starch	21·18
Glucose	20·97
Fat	19·67
Protein	19·25

    Use the data to show that the value for an average diet is accurate to within 5% of any diet based on a single food.   2

    (7)

    (20)

[END OF QUESTION PAPER]

ADVANCED HIGHER

2011

[BLANK PAGE]

X007/701

NATIONAL
QUALIFICATIONS
2011

WEDNESDAY, 1 JUNE
1.00 PM – 3.30 PM

BIOLOGY
ADVANCED HIGHER

SECTION A—Questions 1–25 (25 marks)

Instructions for completion of Section A are given on *Page two*.

SECTIONS B AND C

The answer to each question should be written in ink in the answer book provided. Any additional paper (if used) should be placed inside the front cover of the answer book.

Rough work should be scored through.

Section B (55 marks)

All questions should be attempted. Candidates should note that Question 8 contains a choice.

Question 1 is on Pages 10, 11 and 12. Question 2 is on Page 13. Pages 12 and 13 are fold-out pages.

Section C (20 marks)

Candidates should attempt the questions in **one** unit, **either** Biotechnology **or** Animal Behaviour **or** Physiology, Health and Exercise.

Read carefully

1   Check that the answer sheet provided is for **Biology Advanced Higher (Section A)**.

2   For this section of the examination you must use an **HB pencil** and, where necessary, an eraser.

3   Check that the answer sheet you have been given has **your name**, **date of birth**, **SCN** (Scottish Candidate Number) and **Centre Name** printed on it.

    Do not change any of these details.

4   If any of this information is wrong, tell the Invigilator immediately.

5   If this information is correct, **print** your name and seat number in the boxes provided.

6   The answer to each question is **either** A, B, C or D. Decide what your answer is, then, using your pencil, put a horizontal line in the space provided (see sample question below).

7   There is **only one correct** answer to each question.

8   Any rough working should be done on the question paper or the rough working sheet, **not** on your answer sheet.

9   At the end of the examination, put the **answer sheet for Section A inside the front cover of the answer book**.

Sample Question

Which of the following molecules contains six carbon atoms?

A   Glucose

B   Pyruvic acid

C   Ribulose bisphosphate

D   Acetyl coenzyme A

The correct answer is **A**—Glucose. The answer **A** has been clearly marked in **pencil** with a horizontal line (see below).

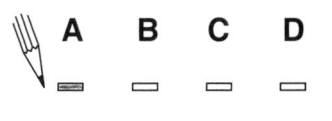

Changing an answer

If you decide to change your answer, carefully erase your first answer and using your pencil, fill in the answer you want. The answer below has been changed to **D**.

SECTION A

All questions in this section should be attempted.

Answers should be given on the separate answer sheet provided.

1. Cellobiose is a disaccharide with glucose monomers joined by a β 1, 4 bond.

   Which of the following represents cellobiose?

   A

   B

   C

   D

2. The following stages occur during the culture of mammalian cells.

   W   Cells flatten

   X   Cells divide

   Y   Cells become confluent

   Z   Cells adhere to surface

   Which line below shows the correct sequence of stages?

   A   X→W→Y→Z

   B   Z→W→X→Y

   C   Z→Y→W→X

   D   X→Y→Z→W

3. A piece of plant tissue prepared for growth under tissue culture conditions is known as

   A   a callus

   B   an explant

   C   a protoplast

   D   a hybrid.

4. The graphs below show the effect of plant growth substances on the development of roots and shoots in plant tissue culture.

   Which of the following treatments produces a root : shoot ratio of 2 : 1?

   A $0 \cdot 2 \, mgl^{-1}$ BAP

   B $0 \cdot 5 \, mgl^{-1}$ BAP

   C $2 \, mgl^{-1}$ NAA

   D $5 \, mgl^{-1}$ NAA

5. In the formation of fats, which type of linkage is formed by the dehydration (condensation) reaction between glycerol and a fatty acid?

   A Phosphodiester

   B Glycosidic

   C Peptide

   D Ester

6. Which of the following describes the structure of guanine?

   A A purine base with a single-ring structure

   B A purine base with a double-ring structure

   C A pyrimidine base with a single-ring structure

   D A pyrimidine base with a double-ring structure

7. An average diploid human cell contains 6×10^9 base pairs of genetic code. Only $1 \cdot 5\%$ of this may be coding for protein.

   How many base pairs code for protein in a human gamete?

   A $4 \cdot 5 \times 10^7$

   B $9 \cdot 0 \times 10^7$

   C $4 \cdot 5 \times 10^8$

   D $9 \cdot 0 \times 10^8$

8. Which of the following is responsible for cell-cell recognition?

   A Glycoprotein

   B Phospholipid

   C Hormones

   D Peptidoglycan

9. The sodium–potassium pump spans the plasma membrane. Various processes involved in the active transport of sodium and potassium ions take place either inside the cell (intracellular) or outside the cell (extracellular).

   Which line in the table correctly applies to the transport of potassium ions?

	Binding location of potassium ions	Conformation of transport protein
A	intracellular	not phosphorylated
B	extracellular	phosphorylated
C	intracellular	phosphorylated
D	extracellular	not phosphorylated

10. Covalent modification can be used to regulate enzyme activity.

    Which of the following is an example of covalent modification?

    A Allosteric modulation

    B End product inhibition

    C Binding of an inhibitor to the active site

    D Addition of a phosphate group by a kinase enzyme

11. The table below shows the results of an investigation into the effects of varying substrate concentration on the activity of the enzyme phosphatase in the presence of inhibitors. The greater the absorbance the more active the enzyme.

	Absorbance		
Substrate concentration (%)	Inhibitor X	Inhibitor Y	Inhibitor Z
0·1	0·03	0·12	0·06
0·25	0·06	0·17	0·06
0·5	0·14	0·21	0·06
1·0	0·30	0·36	0·06

What valid conclusion can be drawn from the results?

A   An increase in substrate concentration reduces the effect of all three inhibitors.

B   All three inhibitors are competitive inhibitors.

C   Inhibitor Z has least effect on enzyme activity.

D   Inhibitor Y has least effect on enzyme activity.

12. A length of DNA is cut into fragments by the restriction enzymes BamHI and EcoRI.

BamHI cut site ▼   EcoRI cut site △

DNA

Which of the following gives the correct number of DNA fragments obtained?

	DNA cut by BamHI only	DNA cut by EcoRI only	DNA cut by both BamHI and EcoRI
A	5	4	8
B	4	5	8
C	5	4	9
D	4	5	9

13. The following diagram represents a food web.

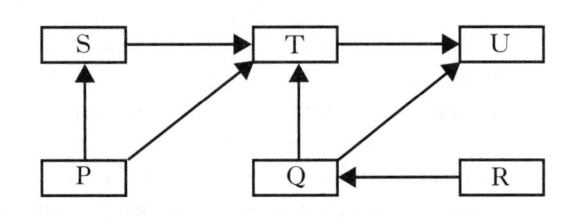

Which line in the table below correctly describes the organisms?

	Producer	Herbivore	Omnivore	Carnivore
A	P	Q	U	S
B	Q	R	S	T
C	R	S	T	U
D	P	U	T	Q

14. A river ecosystem receives about $6\,000\,000\,kJm^{-2}year^{-1}$ of solar energy. Of this energy 98% is **not** used in photosynthesis.

Which of the following shows the amount of energy $(kJm^{-2}year^{-1})$ captured by the producers in this ecosystem?

A   120 000

B   588 000

C   1 200 000

D   5 880 000

15. The percentage of energy transferred from one trophic level to the next describes

A   ecological efficiency

B   growth

C   consumption

D   productivity.

[Turn over

16. The Alcon blue butterfly (*Maculinea alcon*) spends most of its life cycle as a caterpillar associated with usually only one species of red ant (*Myrmica* species). Once the caterpillar chews its way out of the flower where the butterfly laid its eggs, it will die unless ants find it. Ants respond to the caterpillar's secretions and adopt it, taking it into their nest. The caterpillar is fed by worker ants and grows quickly, occasionally eating ant larvae.

Which of the following represents the association between the butterfly species and the ant species?

A   Commensal

B   Mutualistic

C   Parasitic

D   Predatory

17. The diagram below represents part of the nitrogen cycle.

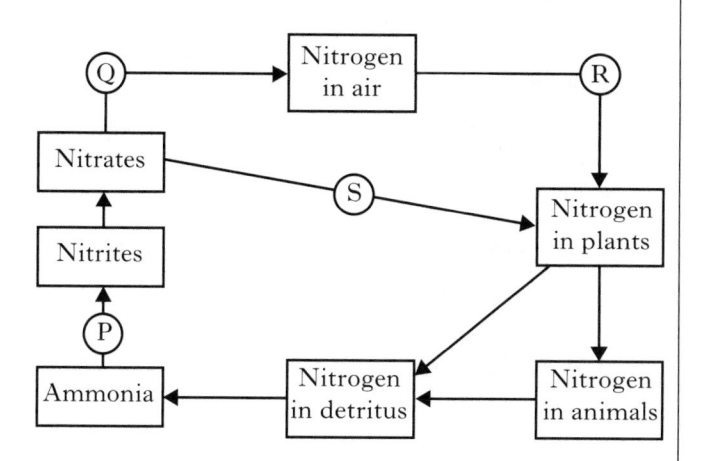

Which of the following stages is likely to involve activity of the enzyme nitrogenase?

A   P

B   Q

C   R

D   S

18. The function of leghaemoglobin is to

A   allow oxygen to react with fixed nitrogen

B   remove oxygen from nitrogen compounds

C   trap nitrogen for use in forming plant proteins

D   trap oxygen to protect bacterial enzymes.

19. The low nitrate content of a marshland soil could result from the activity of

A   *Rhizobium*

B   *Nitrobacter*

C   *Pseudomonas*

D   *Nitrosomonas*.

20. Which of the following is a density-independent effect?

A   An increase in disease decreasing the yield in a crop species

B   An increase in prey numbers increasing the abundance of predators

C   A decrease in grazing increasing the abundance of a plant species

D   A decrease in rainfall increasing the abundance of a plant species

21. The figure below shows two species of butterfly which are bright orange with black markings.

Only the monarch (*Danaus plexippus*) is unpalatable to its predators.

Monarch butterfly

Viceroy butterfly

Which type of mimicry is involved and which species is the mimic?

	Type of mimicry	Mimic
A	Batesian	Monarch
B	Müllerian	Monarch
C	Batesian	Viceroy
D	Müllerian	Viceroy

22. Some insects have a period of dormancy in which a stage of the life cycle is inactive. This type of dormancy is known as

A   hibernation

B   diapause

C   aestivation

D   symbiosis.

23. The figure below shows the general relationships between the internal environment and variation in the external environment of four animals.

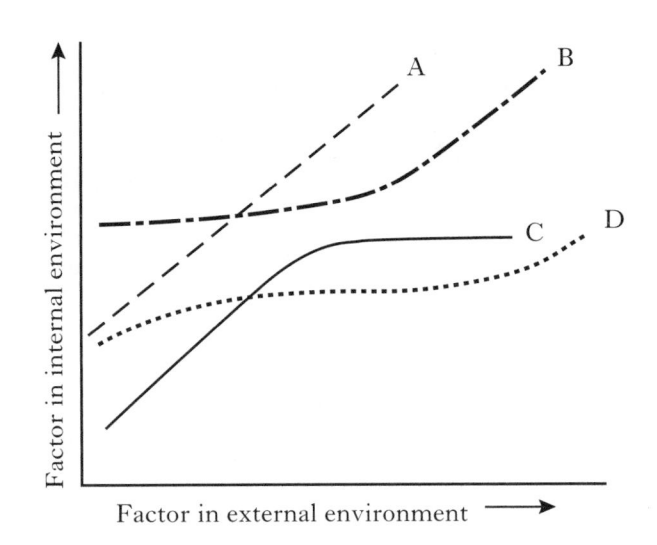

Which animal could occupy the widest range of habitats?

24. Which of the following correctly describes eutrophication?

A   Addition of artificial fertiliser to farmland

B   Nutrient enrichment in ponds

C   Loss of complexity in rivers

D   Algal bloom in lochs

[Turn over

25. Cultivation of soya beans is carried out in areas where hedgerows have been cleared to make large open fields.

The crop is regularly treated with herbicides to which soya bean plants are resistant.

Which line in the table below shows changes that would be expected to occur in an ecosystem when a soya bean farm is set up?

	Soil erosion	Species diversity	Density of insect pest species
A	increase	increase	decrease
B	increase	decrease	increase
C	decrease	decrease	decrease
D	decrease	increase	increase

[END OF SECTION A]

Candidates are reminded that the answer sheet MUST be returned INSIDE the front cover of the answer book.

[Turn over for Section B on Page ten

SECTION B

All questions in this section should be attempted.
All answers must be written clearly and legibly in ink.

1. *Schistosoma* is a parasitic flatworm found in tropical areas throughout the world. The flatworm can live for many years within a host. In humans, if untreated, it causes the disease schistosomiasis (bilharzia), which can be fatal.

    Schistosoma japonicum is found in East Asia; its life cycle is shown in Figure 1. The parasite's eggs hatch in fresh water, releasing a free-living stage that infects a species of freshwater snail. The parasite multiplies asexually within this secondary host before being released into the water as a second free-living stage. This stage is capable of penetrating the skin of humans and other mammals when they are in fresh water. Inside the liver of the mammal, the flatworms develop into sexually mature adults that disperse eggs via the host's large intestine.

Figure 1: Life cycle of *Schistosoma japonicum*

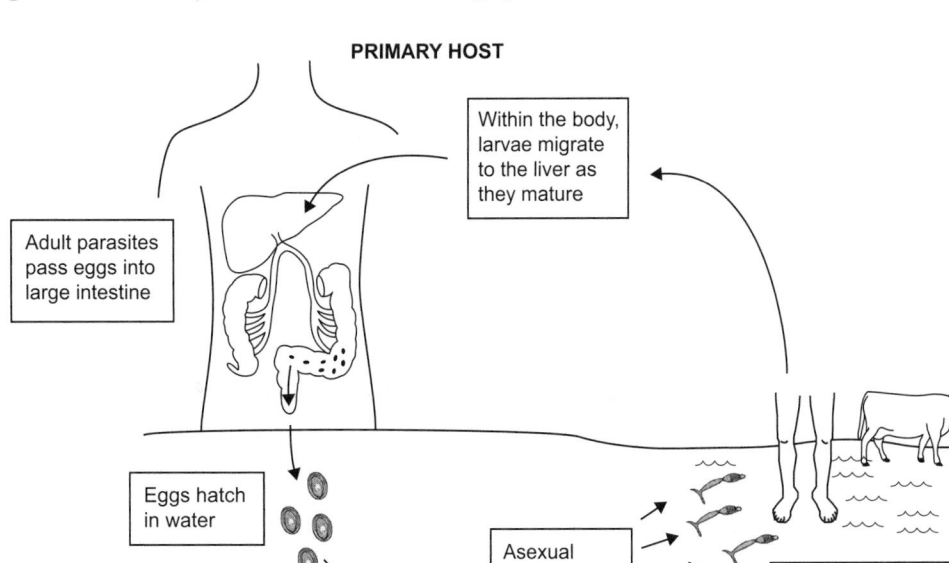

    Successful control of *Schistosoma* is very difficult. Drugs can kill flatworms inside the body but they cannot prevent re-infection. The following factors contribute to high re-infection rates: the parasite has free-living stages; the secondary host can reach high population densities very quickly; untreated, unhygienic humans act as "superspreaders".

    A trial to control *S. japonicum* near a freshwater lake in China compared two pairs of villages given different treatment programmes. Inhabitants of Ximiao and Zhuxi continued to receive the routine annual dose of a drug that kills adult flatworms. Those living in Aiguo and Xinhe were given a programme of intervention that combined the same routine annual drug treatment with the following additional strategies: relevant health education, sanitation, clean bathing water and restrictions on the access of cattle to the lakeside.

    The methods used to evaluate the effectiveness of the intervention programme are shown in the Table and the major findings are shown in Figure 2. The target set for the successful control of *Schistosoma* was to reduce infection in villagers to 1% of the population.

Question 1 (continued)

Table: Methods used to detect *Schistosoma* stages

Stage in life cycle	Detection method for stage
Asexual stage in snail	Dissection of snail samples
Second free-living stage	Dissection of mice exposed in laboratory to samples of lake water
Adult	Non-invasive assessment of human infestation

Figure 2: Infection rates in control and intervention villages

A   Control Villages

B   Intervention Villages

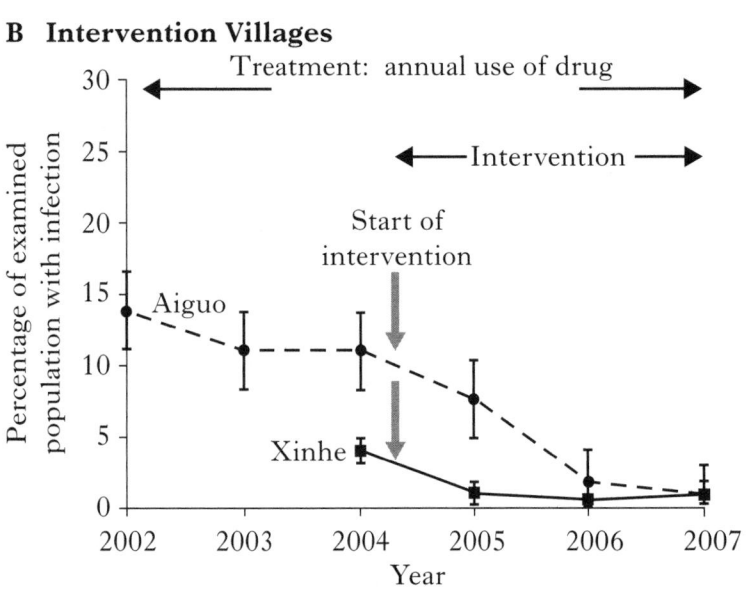

[Question 1 continues on *Page twelve*

Marks

Question 1 (continued)

(*a*)   (i)   Explain what is meant by the term parasitism.   2

    (ii)   *Schistosoma* has free-living stages but can only feed or reproduce when in contact with a host. What term is used to describe this form of parasitism?   1

(*b*)   One of the keys to the successful control of *Schistosoma* is to reduce the number of "superspreaders".

    (i)   Suggest a "non-invasive assessment" for identifying superspreaders.   1

    (ii)   Give **two** aspects of the intervention designed to tackle superspreaders.   2

(*c*)   (i)   Use the data from the trial to show that the intervention is needed to achieve the 1% target for infection.   2

    (ii)   Comment on the reliability of the results.   1

(*d*)   Attempts have been made to control *Schistosoma* through the use of molluscicides to kill the secondary host. Using the information, suggest why this method of control is unlikely to be successful with reference to

    (i)   the secondary host;   1

    (ii)   the parasite.   1

(*e*)   Explain how the broad host specificity of *S. japonicum* has influenced both the design of the intervention programme and the methods for measuring its effectiveness.   3

(14)

[Question 2 is on fold-out *Page thirteen*

Marks

2. The graph below shows variation in global atmospheric carbon dioxide concentration during a fifty year period. Seasonal variation occurs because there is much more green plant biomass in the northern hemisphere than in the southern hemisphere. The underlying trend, however, reveals an increase in concentration.

(a) Which **two** cellular processes are responsible for the seasonal variation in carbon dioxide concentration of the atmosphere?

1

(b) Using the trend line, calculate the percentage increase in the carbon dioxide concentration between 1965 and 1995.

1

(c) The increasing carbon dioxide concentration contributes to the enhanced greenhouse effect.

   (i) Explain what is meant by the term *enhanced* in relation to the greenhouse effect.

1

   (ii) Name a gas, other than carbon dioxide, that contributes to the enhanced greenhouse effect.

1

(4)

Marks

3. Soils that have developed from serpentine rocks have a naturally low abundance of minerals such as calcium, nitrogen, phosphorus and potassium, and a high abundance of potentially toxic metals such as nickel. The succession of serpentine plant communities shows little facilitation and is limited by the regular input of toxic minerals from the erosion of the rock. The climax vegetation that develops tends to be sparse and species present have unusual adaptations to cope with the high concentrations of metal in the soil.

   (*a*) (i)   What is meant by facilitation in succession?   1

   (ii)   What term describes a succession influenced by external factors such as erosion?   1

   (*b*) The flowering herb *Alyssum bertolonii* is favoured in serpentine soils because it can isolate absorbed nickel into specialised leaf hair cells. As a result, its dry mass can be as high as 3% nickel. Most other species are susceptible to nickel poisoning at much lower concentrations.

   (i)   What term describes the increasing levels of nickel found in *A. bertolonii*?   1

   (ii)   Explain why a serpentine climax community is unlikely to have many trophic levels.   1

   (iii)   Suggest why *A. bertolonii* could be used as an indicator species.   1

   (5)

4. Discuss the concept of niche with reference to the competitive exclusion principle.   **(4)**

Marks

5. Myoglobin and haemoglobin are oxygen-carrying proteins. Myoglobin has one polypeptide chain and is found in muscle. Haemoglobin has four polypeptide chains and is found in red blood cells. The tertiary structures of the myoglobin and the haemoglobin chains are very similar. Each chain has one binding site for oxygen.

The proportion of binding sites occupied by oxygen is known as *saturation*.

$$\text{Saturation} = \frac{\text{number of oxygen binding sites occupied}}{\text{total number of oxygen binding sites}}$$

The graph shows the binding of oxygen to haemoglobin and myoglobin as the available oxygen is increased.

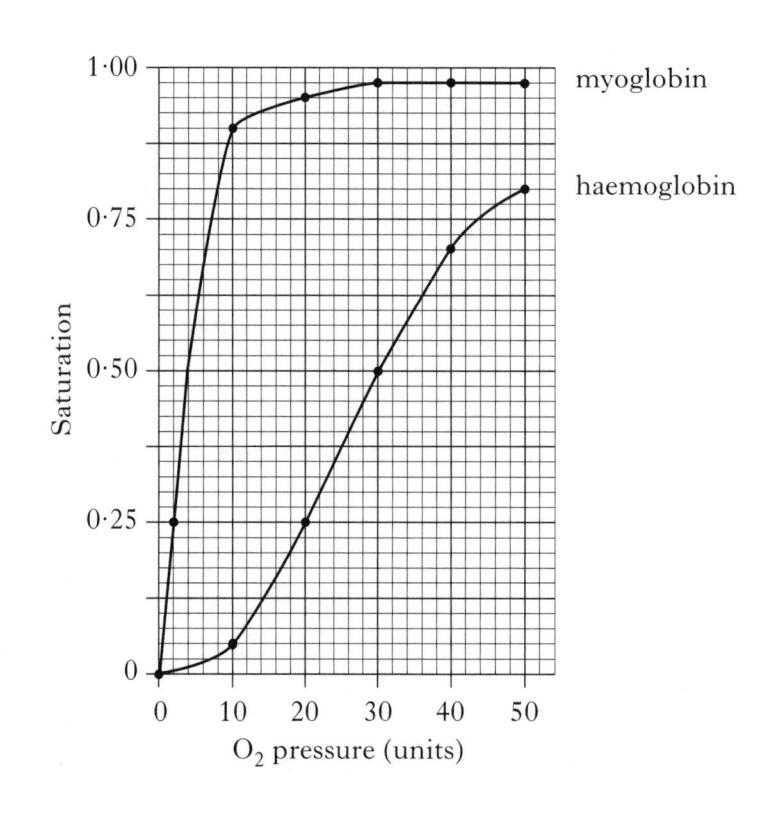

(a) (i) Use data to compare the saturation of myoglobin and haemoglobin between 0 and 30 units.   1

   (ii) Explain how the information shows that quaternary structure affects the binding of oxygen to haemoglobin.   2

(b) Use the formula to calculate the change in the number of oxygen molecules bound to haemoglobin as the oxygen pressure is reduced from 30 to 20 units.   1

(c) Haem groups are an example of non-polypeptide components present in proteins. What term describes such components?   1

(5)

[Turn over

Marks

6. Gamma-aminobutyric acid (GABA) is a neurotransmitter that functions as a signalling molecule in the central nervous system. GABA binds to a receptor protein located in the plasma membrane of target cells as shown in Figure 1. Binding of a GABA molecule opens a channel that allows chloride ions (Cl⁻) to enter the cell.

Figure 1   **Figure 2**

Benzodiazepines are sedative drugs that bind to the receptor protein and increase its affinity for GABA. These drugs act as allosteric modulators by binding at a site that is distinct from the GABA-binding site. Figure 2 above shows the movement of chloride ions through the channel as GABA is increased with and without the drug being present.

(a) (i) State why neurotransmitters such as GABA cannot cross the membrane. 1

   (ii) What term describes the action of membrane receptors in which signal binding triggers an event in the cytoplasm that alters the behaviour of the cell? 1

(b) (i) How does the information in Figure 2 show that the affinity of the receptor for GABA has been increased by the drug? 1

   (ii) How might the binding of benzodiazepine to the modulatory site increase the affinity of the receptor for GABA? 1

(4)

Marks

7. Cystic fibrosis is caused by mutation within the gene encoding the CFTR protein. The most common mutation in this gene is a three base-pair deletion that results in the loss of one amino acid from the CFTR protein. This deletion, ΔF508, accounts for about 70% of mutations in cystic fibrosis.

   A screening test for cystic fibrosis uses the polymerase chain reaction (PCR) to amplify part of the *CFTR* gene containing the mutation.

   (*a*) Describe the features of primers used in PCR.   2

   (*b*) Give **one** technique that could be used in the detection of the mutation following PCR.   1

   (*c*) What information should be given to someone during counselling, following a negative screening result for ΔF508?   1

   (4)

8. Answer **either** A **or** B.

   A. Compare prokaryotic and eukaryotic cells under the following headings:

      (i)   organisation of genetic material;   5

     (ii)   ultrastructure and other features.   10

   OR   **(15)**

   B. Write notes on the cell cycle and its control under the following headings:

      (i)   interphase;   5

     (ii)   mitosis;   5

    (iii)   mutations.   5

   (15)

[END OF SECTION B]

[Turn over for Section C

SECTION C

Candidates should attempt questions on <u>one</u> unit, <u>either</u> Biotechnology <u>or</u> Animal Behaviour <u>or</u> Physiology, Health and Exercise.

The questions on Biotechnology can be found on pages 18–21.

The questions on Animal Behaviour can be found on pages 22–25.

The questions on Physiology, Health and Exercise can be found on pages 26–28.

All answers must be written clearly and legibly in ink.

Labelled diagrams may be used where appropriate.

BIOTECHNOLOGY

Marks

1. The figure shows stages involved in the commercial production of an antibiotic.

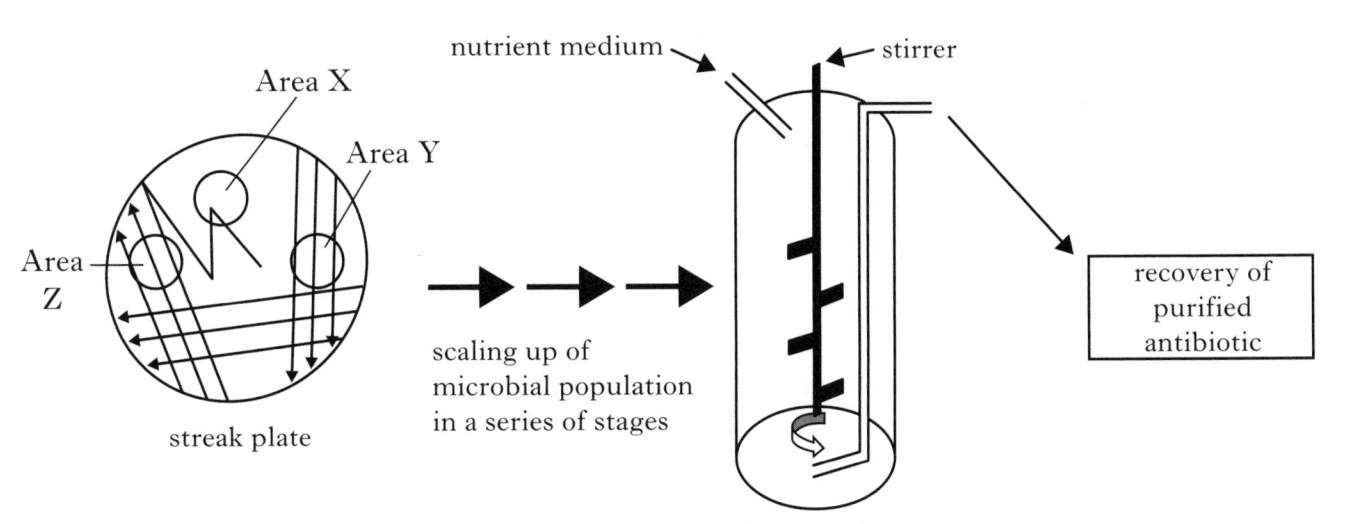

(a) Name a commercially produced antibiotic and the type of micro-organism used in its production.   1

(b) The scaling up process above is started using cells from a single isolated colony.

    (i) Explain why it is necessary to use a single colony isolate.   1

    (ii) Which one of the labelled areas on the streak plate would be most likely to have such a colony?   1

(c) Give **one** reason why the culture in the fermentation vessel is stirred.   1

(d) Give **one** process involved in the recovery of the antibiotic.   1

Marks

BIOTECHNOLOGY (continued)

1.   (continued)

   (*e*)   The figure shows changes in the culture medium during the production of an antibiotic in a fermentation vessel.

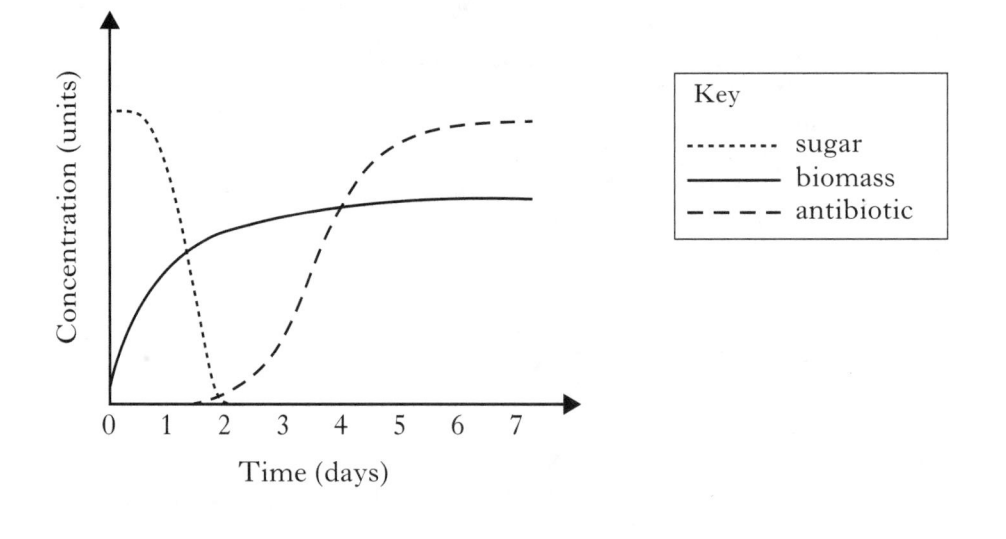

   From the figure, give **two** pieces of evidence to indicate that this antibiotic is a secondary metabolite.

2

(7)

[Turn over

Marks

BIOTECHNOLOGY (continued)

2. The diagram shows stages in the production of monoclonal antibodies.

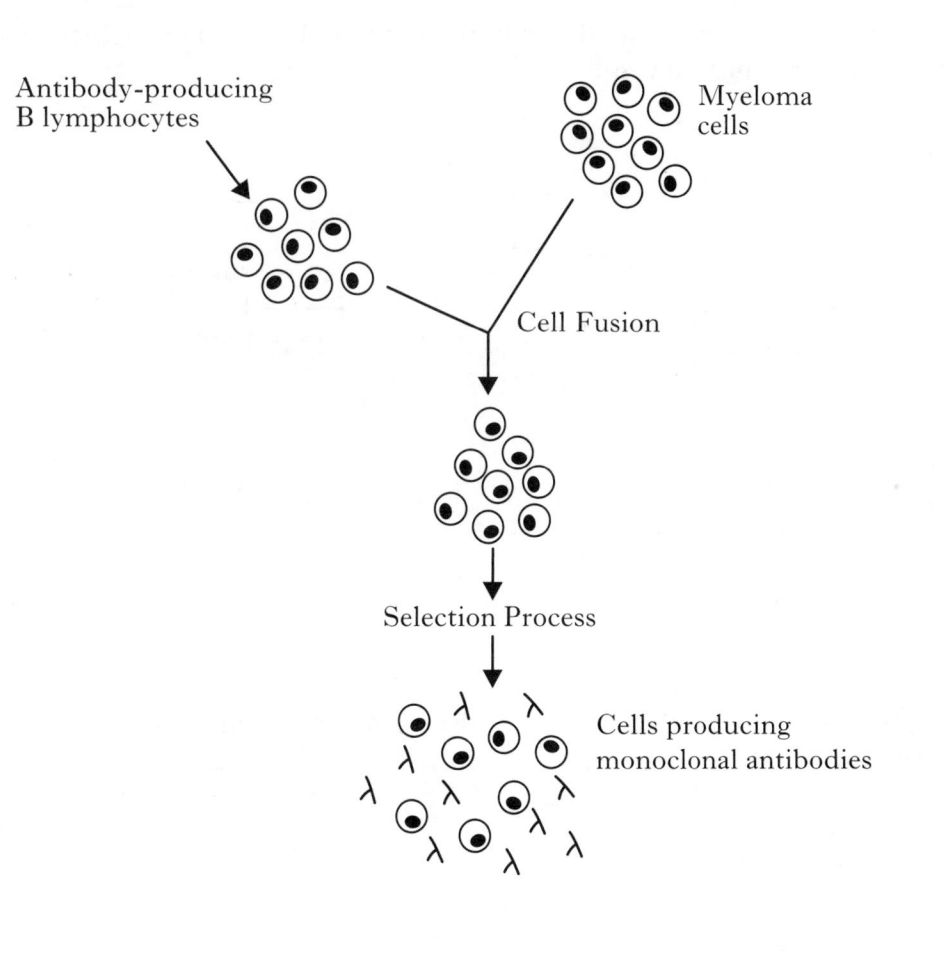

(a) Describe how the B lymphocytes shown above would have been produced.   2

(b) Name the chemical used to bring about the fusion of B lymphocytes and myeloma cells.   1

(c) Give **one** use of monoclonal antibodies in the **treatment** of disease.   1

     (4)

3. The chemical composition of plant cell walls causes problems in the commercial production of fruit juices. Identify the problems and outline how enzymes are used to overcome them.   (5)

BIOTECHNOLOGY (continued)

Marks

4. Several studies have demonstrated the antimicrobial activity of oils extracted from plants. One such study investigated the bactericidal activity of an oil from cinnamon bark on the bacterium, methicillin-resistant *Staphylococcus aureus* (MRSA). The oil was added to broth containing an inoculum of MRSA.

(a) Viable counts were made at intervals over a one hour period.

What is meant by a viable count? **1**

(b) The graph below shows data for different concentrations of the cinnamon bark oil and a control with no oil. Log units are powers of ten.

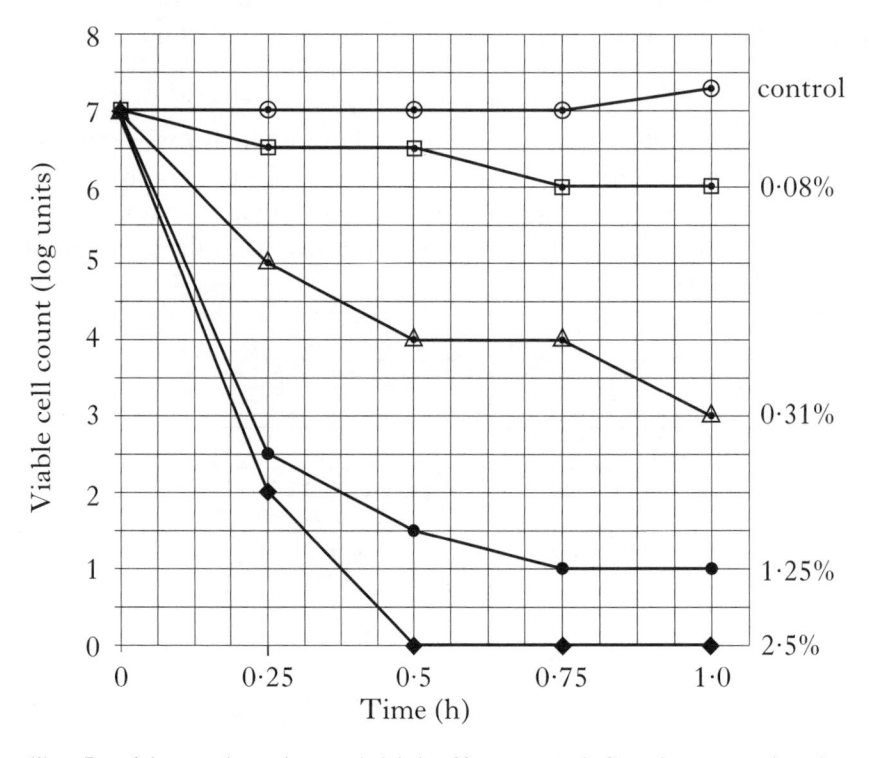

(i) In this study a bactericidal effect was defined as a reduction, over a one hour period, of 5 log units from the initial viable count.

Identify which of the oil treatments are bactericidal. **1**

(ii) What aspect of the procedure was necessary to ensure that a valid comparison was made between the control and the treatments with essential oil? **1**

(iii) By how many cells has the starting population been reduced in the 0·08% treatment after the first hour? **1**

(4)

[End of *Biotechnology* questions. *Animal Behaviour* questions start on Page 22]

(20)

SECTION C (continued)

ANIMAL BEHAVIOUR

1.   Northwestern crows (*Corvus caurinus*) can be observed feeding on the beaches of British Columbia in Canada. They search mainly for whelks (*Thais lamellosa*).

Northwestern crow and whelk prey (not to scale)

The crows search only for the largest whelks. After finding a whelk, they take off with it and fly vertically upwards before dropping it onto a rock. This is repeated until the whelk's shell is broken. Steep ascending flight of this kind is energetically expensive. The crows are very persistent and may drop a single whelk up to 20 times before the shell breaks.

(a)   The graph below shows the results of an experiment in which **researchers** dropped small, medium and large whelks from different heights. In the graph, "Total height" is obtained by combining the number of drops at each height required to break the whelk. The arrow on the X axis indicates the mean height of drop actually observed when **crows** drop whelks.

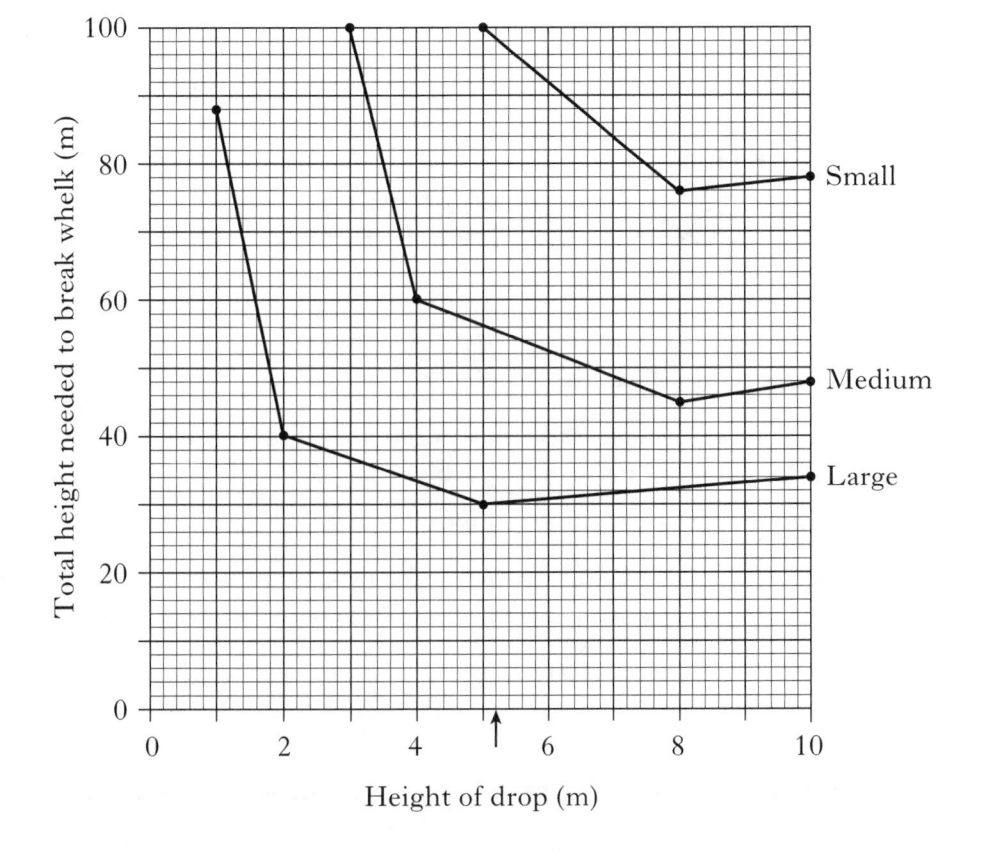

Page twenty-two

Marks

ANIMAL BEHAVIOUR (continued)

1. **(*a*) (continued)**

    (i) On average, how many times would a medium-sized whelk need to be dropped from a height of 4 m in order to break?   **1**

    (ii) From the information provided, suggest why crows take only the largest whelks.   **1**

  (*b*) Use the concept of optimal foraging to explain the observation that crows drop whelks from an average height of 5·2 m.   **2**

  (*c*) Apart from energy content and handling time, what other aspect of foraging behaviour is likely to be of significance in determining a predator's choice of prey?   **1**

                           (5)

2. "All development depends on both nature and nurture." (R. Hinde)

    With reference to life span, compare the roles of nature and nurture in the behavioural development of adult invertebrates and primates.   **(5)**

[Turn over

Marks

ANIMAL BEHAVIOUR (continued)

3. The broad-nosed pipefish (*Syngnathus typhle*) can be found along many coasts and estuaries in the British Isles. In this species, "normal" sex roles are reversed: females compete with each other for males and it is the males that are selective. During mating, the female transfers her eggs into a brood pouch in the male where they are then fertilised and nourished. The males provide parental care for the young.

   All pipefish are susceptible to infestation by a parasite that induces the formation of visible black spots on the skin.

   Figure: Pipefish showing signs of parasite infestation

   When females are infected, egg production decreases as the parasite load increases. High intensity infections may kill the fish host.

   Experiments were carried out to discover male responses to spotted females that were either naturally infected or had been artificially tattooed using ink dissolved in a solvent. In both situations, it was found that males selected females with fewer or no black spots. Behavioural interactions between males, however, were not influenced by the presence or absence of spots on the males.

   (a) During mating, the fish are more vulnerable to predators.

      (i) Explain how the male's preference for healthy females allows him to maximise his reproductive fitness.   **2**

      (ii) Explain why the genes controlling this behaviour might be described as "selfish".   **1**

   (b) Give **one** aspect of behaviour that contributes to the high level of parental investment shown by the male pipefish.   **1**

   (c) The parasite cannot be transmitted directly from one fish to another.

      Which aspect of pipefish behaviour is consistent with this observation?   **1**

   (d) Suggest a control that should be used in the experiment involving tattooed spots.   **1**

   (e) In the experiments, fish were arranged so that males could see females but females could not see males. Explain why this would strengthen the conclusion that males select against parasitised females using visual stimuli.   **1**

   (7)

Marks

ANIMAL BEHAVIOUR (continued)

4. Cannibalism occurs when animals eat other animals of their own species. Willow leaf beetles, *Plagiodera versicolora*, lay eggs in clutches (groups). Females may have mated once or several times so clutches contain a mixture of half and full siblings. This means that the coefficient of relatedness, **r**, varies between 0·25 and 0·5.

   Larvae that hatch first eat unhatched eggs from the same clutch. 24 hours after hatching, cannibals are 30% heavier than non-cannibals.

   The scatterplot shows cannibalism rate and clutch relatedness for a number of populations.

   Figure: Cannibalism rate versus average clutch relatedness for each of eight populations

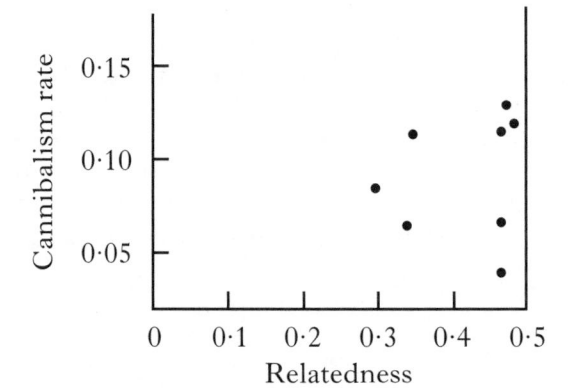

   (a) Why do full siblings have a coefficient of relatedness of 0·5? 1

   (b) A hypothesis from Hamilton's rule would be that cannibalistic larvae should not eat close relatives.

      (i) What is meant by Hamilton's rule? 1

      (ii) What evidence from the graph contradicts the hypothesis? 1

   (3)

   (20)

[End of *Animal Behaviour* questions. *Physiology, Health and Exercise* questions start on Page 26]

[Turn over

SECTION C (continued)   *Marks*

PHYSIOLOGY, HEALTH AND EXERCISE

1. Describe how atherosclerosis can lead to myocardial infarction.   **(4)**

2. (a) To reduce the risk of cardiovascular disease, individuals are encouraged to improve the ratio of high-density lipoprotein (HDL) to low-density lipoprotein (LDL).

    Give **two** lifestyle factors that can be changed to improve the ratio of HDL:LDL.   **2**

    (b) Cholesterol in the blood is associated with HDL, LDL and triglycerides. Treatment with *statin* medication aims to improve the ratio of HDL to LDL by reducing cholesterol production.

    The data below show the blood lipid profiles of a patient before and after two years of statin medication, and the normal range of values for a healthy individual.

Blood lipid	Concentration (mmol/l)		
	Before treatment	*After treatment*	*Normal range values*
Total cholesterol	8·5	5·5	3·0 – 5·0
HDL	1·9	1·8	1·0 – 2·2
LDL		2·9	2·0 – 3·4
Triglycerides	1·5	1·7	0·3 – 2·5
Total cholesterol/HDL	4·5	3·1	about 3·0

    (i) LDL is not measured directly, it is calculated from other values using the formula below.

    LDL = (Total – HDL) – (Triglycerides / 2·2)

    Calculate the LDL value before treatment.   **1**

    (ii) Select **two** pieces of evidence to show that statin treatment has reduced the risk of cardiovascular disease.   **2**

    (iii) The aim for statin treatment is to increase the proportion of HDL to over 30% of the total. Use the data to show that this has been achieved.   **1**

    (6)

Marks

PHYSIOLOGY, HEALTH AND EXERCISE (continued)

3. (*a*) Blood glucose concentration increases after a meal.

Describe the events that bring blood glucose concentration back to normal. **2**

(*b*) In an *oral glucose tolerance test*, an individual has "impaired glucose tolerance" when results are in the range 7·8 to 11·0 mmol/l. A result in this range is referred to as *pre-diabetic*. If untreated, pre-diabetes leads to Type 2 diabetes (NIDDM).

The underlying cause of impaired glucose tolerance is insulin resistance.

(i) Explain why cells become less sensitive to insulin in individuals with insulin resistance. **1**

(ii) For people with pre-diabetes, explain why there would be a long-term benefit from reducing a high waist to hip ratio. **2**

(5)

[**Turn over for Question 4 on *Page twenty-eight***

Marks

PHYSIOLOGY, HEALTH AND EXERCISE (continued)

4. (a) Why does taking part in sporting activities during adolescence reduce the risk of osteoporosis–related fractures in later life?

    2

    (b) The figure below shows the results of a study comparing bone mineral density of groups of women involved in different types of sport. The values show mean percentage difference in bone mineral density between the athletes and a control group who have an inactive lifestyle.

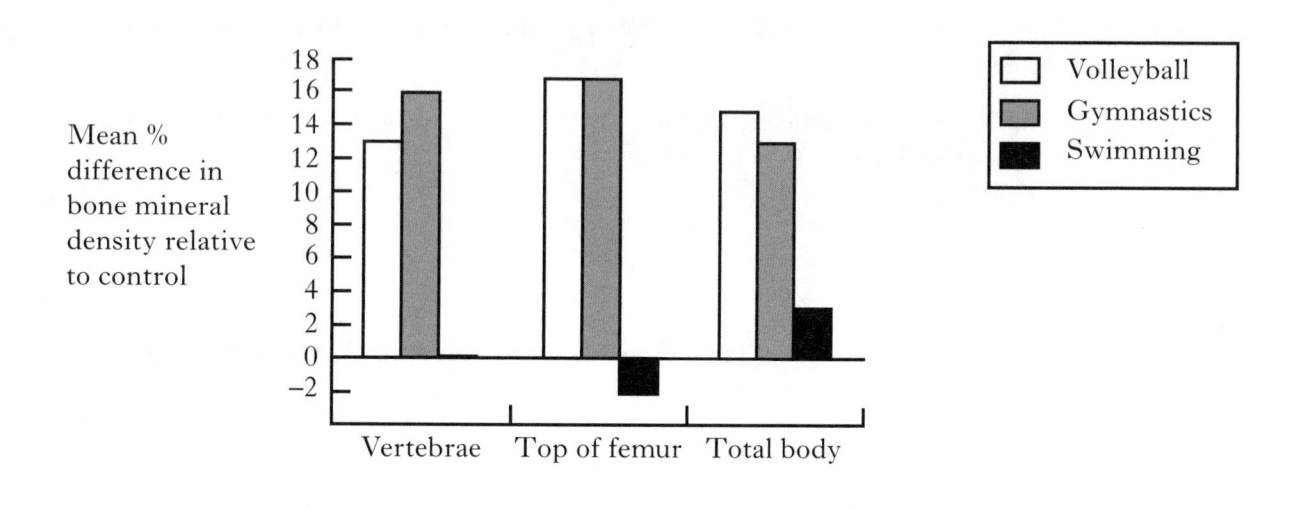

    (i) Suggest why the study focuses on bone mineral density of vertebrae and the top of the femur (thigh).

    1

    (ii) Explain why swimmers are included in the study.

    1

    (iii) The data suggest that swimming has a negative effect on bone mineral density at the top of the femur. What other information would be required to judge if the results are statistically significant?

    1

    (5)

    (20)

[END OF QUESTION PAPER]

[BLANK PAGE]

Acknowledgements

Permission has been sought from all relevant copyright holders and Bright Red Publishing is grateful for the use of the following:

An extract from 'From structure to disease: the evolving tale of aquaporin biology' by Landon S. King, David Kozono and Peter Agre, reprinted by permission from MacMillan Publishers Ltd: *Nature Reviews Molecular Cell Biology*, copyright © 2004 (2008 page 10);

A table adapted from 'Diffusional water permeability of human erythrocytes and their ghosts' by J Brahm, © Brahm 1982. Originally published in *The Journal of General Physiology 79* 791–819 (2008 page 10);

A picture from *Physiological Mini-Reviews* Vol 1, No 10, May 2006 by A Guttierrez. Published by The Argentine Physiological Society (2008 page 10);

A picture from 'Severely Impaired Urinary Concentrating Ability in Transgenic Mice Lacking Aquaporin-1 Water Channels' by Tonghui Ma, Baoxue Yang, Annemarie Gillespie, Elaine J. Carlson, Charles J. Epstein and A. S. Verkman. Published in *Journal of Biological Chemistry* 20 February 1998. Copyright © 1998, by the American Society for Biochemistry and Molecular Biology (2008 page 11).

SQA ADVANCED HIGHER
BIOLOGY 2007–2011

SECTION A

1. C	14. A
2. C	15. B
3. D	16. A
4. A	17. B
5. C	18. D
6. C	19. B
7. B	20. D
8. A	21. A
9. D	22. D
10. A	23. C
11. D	24. B
12. B	25. B
13. C	

SECTION B

1. (a) (i) Exotic/alien (species)
   (ii) Reduction/population change/elimination/ extinction of native species
       loss of biodiversity
       or Competitive exclusion/take over niche
       or Alteration of community structure/ habitat change

   (b) (i) Variable number of trap nights (in each sweep)
       or
       To give a standard/valid/fair/easier way to compare data
       (ii) Identify the change in the trend/capture rates after September as the mind changing/ significant finding
       Trend down and up – both quantifications to illustrate.
       In sweeps 1–4 capture rates reduced from 589 to 2 (per 10 000) trap nights showing population decline.
       In sweeps 5–6 capture rates increased to 15 (per 10 000) trap nights showing population increase.

   (c) Trapping successful (capture rate drops) prior to breeding (in November).

       or After breeding begins (in November) population recovers.

   (d) (i) Percentage cover values (in Table 2) are equivalent to capture frequencies expressed as percentages
       Illustrative quantification; eg % predicted captures in ebony forest
       $(192/524) \times 100 = 36{\cdot}6 = 37\%$,
       Percentage cover = 37%
       (ii) *Leucaena* forest
       (iii) Larger numbers *than expected* trapped in weeded forest/
       Leucaena forest (both products of human activity)
       or
       correct reference to densities

(e) Specific toxicity to target organism/avoiding poisoning of/nor not harmful to other species
    or Non-persistent/biodegradable/non-biomagnified

(f) (Relationship where) one (species/organism) benefits but the other neither benefits nor loses (= unaffected)

(g) *Any one from:*
    • Encourage population increase in natural predator.
    • Introduce a predator/other measures to increase death rate or decrease birth rate
    • Check baggage etc of visitors/measures to decrease immigration

2. (a) Detritivores

   (b) *Any two from:*
       Larger detritivores/invertebrates/ organisms (get into the 7mm bag) and break down/fragment the litter
       or more organisms enter the 7mm bag, so more breakdown occurs.

       Increases surface area for decomposer action **or** increased surface area increases rate of decomposition.

       In 7mm bag there is both breakdown and decomposition whereas there is only decomposition in the 1 mm bag

       In 7mm bag there is both internal and external digestion whereas in the 1 mm bag there is external only

   (c) Minerals/any specific mineral eg nitrate/phosphate etc
       or Carbon dioxide
       or Heat (energy)
       or Water
       or Humus

   (d) Degradative/heterotrophic succession

3. 1. Regulator maintains **constant** internal environment
      or Regulator uses homeostatic control.

   2. Osmoregulator defined as organism able to control water balance.

   3. Thermoregulator defined as organism able to keep (body) T constant.

   4. Regulators occupy wider range of habitats.

   5. (High) energy costs of homeostasis/regulation.

   6. Illustrative comment on osmoregulation.

   7. Illustrative comment on thermoregulation.

4. (a) Increased (intensity of) effect as density increased
       or The more flatworms there are *per sheep*, the lower the rate of egg production *per worm*
       or Increasing competition for resource where this is described as density dependent

   (b) Transmission to new host
       or as a vector
       or dispersal

   (c) Host healthy - parasite harmful but not lethal whereas host unhealthy the parasite may be lethal/cause a bigger infestation.

(d) *Reasonable management practice eg:*
vaccination
molluscicide
fluke treatment
crop rotation
treatment of food/surroundings/animal to kill parasite/isolation etc

5. (a) Kinase phosphorylates/adds phosphate (the Rb protein) which keeps cells out of the cycle/stops regulatory proteins switching on division/blocks regulatory proteins that promote proliferation/keeps the brakes on division

   (b) Mutations in both alleles/copies (of Rb gene) are needed for it to affect cell proliferation whereas proto-oncogenes need one.
   or Rb protein acts as an inhibitor of/Rb gene inhibits cell proliferation where oncogenes promote.
   or proto-oncogenes are proliferation genes, Rb genes are anti-proliferation
   or Both Rb alleles mutating is recessive effect and proto-oncogene mutation is a dominant

6. (a) Prokaryotic - *any two from:*
   - no nuclear membrane/true nucleus/would have nucleoid
   - no membrane bound organelles
   - no organelles except ribosomes
   - no histones/nucleosomes/chromosomes
   - contain plasmids
   - has wall of peptidoglycan

   (b) Medium:cytoplasm:vacuole = 1:3:99

   (c) Pump moves sodium ions out (of cytoplasm) and brings potassium in
   No pump in pm:
   Sodium concentration in cytoplasm (0·6) is higher than the medium (0·2)
   or Na and K are both higher than medium, so not exchanged
   Possible pump at vacuole:
   Na high in vacuole low in cytoplasm, unlike K

7. (a) It has charge/there is an electric current through the gel/gel is porous

   (b) The mutation increases the fragment size from allele B2. (both alleles are present because) the digest produced/gel shows two fragment sizes/lengths **or** two bands

   (c) B2B2

   (d) *Any two from:*
   1, 3 or 6

8. (a) (i)   Control mechanisms of the cell cycle:
   Any six from nine:
   1. Checkpoint **near/before** the end of G1 assesses size
   2. Ensures sufficient (mass) to form two daughter cells/to allow cell division/for cycle to proceed
   3. Checkpoint during G2 controls entry to mitosis
   4. DNA replication assessed
   5. So each daughter cell receives complete genome/copy of DNA
   6. Mitosis promoting factor/MPF necessary for entry into mitosis
   7. MPF is a protein (complex)
   8. Checkpoint during/in metaphase (of mitosis) controls entry to anaphase/ cytokinesis/end of mitosis
   9. M checkpoint checks chromosome alignment/ensures each daughter cell receives one chromatid from each chromosome

   (ii)   Culturing of mammalian cells:
   Any nine from the following fourteen:
   1. Cells grown under aseptic conditions **and** one example
   2. Mammalian cells need growth factors **or** complex growth medium
   3. (provided in medium by) addition of serum/FBS
   4. Any 2 'simple' components from salts, amino acids, vitamins, glucose, water
   5. Antibiotics added to prevent bacterial growth
   6. Use of proteolytic enzyme to release cells from source tissue
   7. (Normal) cells need surface to adhere to/ need anchorage (converse for tumour cells)
   8. Cells spread/flatten out (then)
   9. Mitosis/divide until growth is confluent
   10. (Normal) cells grow as a monolayer
   11. Normal cells divide a certain number of times then die
   12. Tumour/mutated cells used because they are 'immortal'/unlimited division
   13. Single cells isolated and cultured to give clones/cell lines
   14. Application of cell culture: tissue for skin grafts; antibody production; cell lines for research

   (b) (i)   The structure of phospholipids:
   Any six from nine:
   1. Diagram or description of head, tail, hydrophobic, hydrophilic
   2. Phospholipid has glycerol, 2 fatty acids and phosphate
   3. Glycerol structure shown correctly or described (carbons 1, 2 3, and OH attached)
   4. (Fatty acids and phosphate joined by) ester bonds to glycerol
   5. Ester bonds shown or described as condensation reaction between -OH of acid and -OH of alcohol (between OHs of glycerol and acidic ends of fatty acids)
   6. Fatty acids hydrophobic
   7. (Usually) one saturated one unsaturated
   8. Choline attached to phosphate
   9. Phosphate (and choline are) soluble/ hydrophilic/polar

   (ii)   The composition of the plasma membrane:
   Any three from the following five:
   1. Model of membrane is described as *fluid mosaic*
   2. Description or diagram of bilayer showing orientation of phospholipids - hydrophobic (tails) and hydrophilic (heads) labelled
   3. Proteins shown/described as integral (intrinsic, transmembrane) and peripheral (extrinsic)
   4. Lipid bilayer held together by hydrophobic interactions
   5. Presence of cholesterol/cholesterol affects membrane fluidity

   (iii)   Functions of membrane proteins:
   Any six from the following nine:
   1. Attachment to cytoskeleton
   2. Attachment to extracellular/matrix proteins
   3. Junctions between cells/adhesion to each other
   4. Transport of materials across membrane/into and out of cell or organelles
   5. Channels/carriers facilitate/speed up/ enhance passively/by diffusion/or concentration gradient idea

6. Pumps/sodium-potassium pump for moving ions **or** pumps are proteins for active transport
7. Membrane-bound enzymes
8. Receptors for (hydrophilic) cell signals/hormones
9. Glycoprotein/or description of structure for cell-cell recognition

SECTION C

Biotechnology

1. (a) Sterilise air in/equipment/medium
   Aseptic transfers
   Pure inoculum

   (b) (Cold water flowing through it) cools fermenter to keep the temperature low/constant/regulated
   or fermentation/respiration generates heat so cold water is needed.

   (c) (i) subtilisin/amylase
             cellulase
             pectinase
             polygalacturonase
             lactase/β-galactosidase
             invertase/sucrase
             restriction enzymes
       (ii) chymosin
             rennin substitutes
             gluconase
             amyloglucosidase

2. *Any five from:*
   1. Requires down-stream processing.
   2. **Separation** of cells to obtain cell free solution by flocculation - to precipitate cells
      or using (ultra)filtration/centrifugation/pass culture through bed of silica.
   3. **Extraction** of antibiotic from medium in (organic) solvent if soluble
      or *any one from* adsorption/ion exchange/chemical precipitation by addition of compounds/reverse osmosis/dialysis if not solvent-soluble
   4. **Concentration** to obtain crude solute/product by removal of solvent/liquid
   5. Concentration by distillation
      or ultrafiltration/membrane filtration
      or (vacuum) evaporation
      or drying
   6. **Purification:** separation by chromatography
      or crystallisation
   7. Naming three stages without description

3. (a) Total count - living and dead/all cells included

   Viable count - only living cells **or** colonies where each has arisen from one living/viable cell

   (b) Culture B grows rapidly/exponentially to limit/max/constant. Culture C increases at lower rate and does not reach a maximum.

   B maximum is at 120 mins and 150×10^6 cells. C 30×10^6 cells at 120 mins /140×10^6 at end/220 mins.

   (c) (i) 80min = 50 cells, 100min = 100 cells
            so g = 20min = 0.333hr
            k = 0.693/0.333
            = **2.08/2·079/2.1**
       (ii) k will decrease

(d) (CAP/activator protein is activated by cAMP.)
   • Activated CAP binds (to DNA).
   • β-galactosidase gene transcribed
     or CAP therefore exerts positive control

4. (a) Resistance is lost.
   Tetracycline resistance gene would be disabled.
   Bacteria taking up the plasmid would not be resistant.

   (b) These colonies contain the modified plasmids.
   Because they have ampicillin resistance but not tetracycline resistance.
   or They grow on plate X but not on plate Y.

   (c) *Any one from:*
   Transfer of nif gene/nitrogenase gene/enhancing nitrogen fixation
   Insecticidal plants
   Frost resistance
   Transfer of bacterial toxin to protect from insect damage
   Bovine somatotrophin (BST).

Animal Behaviour

1. (a) Ethogram

   (b) Example: pout/grin/fear/begging/excitement
   Explanation: relating animal behaviour to human experience/attributes/motives

   (c) Grooming/sexual presentation/sexual intercourse/appeasement gesture

2. (a) *Any two points from:*
   Black eyebar provokes/has increased attacks per minute/rate and orange spots a reduction

   Black eyebar model: attacks increase to 3·6/min (or by 80%)
   Orange spot model: decreased to 1/min (or by 50%)

   Neither response showed any delay (latency)

   With both models, normal level reached in same time (32/33 min)

   (b) Orange spots alone suggest egg laying, so no threat **or** Retreating male would show this pattern, so no threat.

   (c) Increased reproductive success/more chance of fathering offspring/greater access to females

   (d) (Dimorphic because) territorial males different in appearance from female
   or
   (Not dimorphic because) non-territorial male resembles female
   or Some males resemble females and others don't.

   (e) Genetic influence - fish reared alone still responded to black eyebar model (or male of same species) with attack.
   Environmental/learned influence - fish reared by another species show attack response towards male of foster species.

3. (a) Improved chances of survival of young

   (b) Mimicry/camouflage/masquerade

   (c) Gape acts as <u>sign stimulus</u> (for host to feed young cuckoo)
   or Releaser causes host to follow <u>fixed action pattern</u> (and feed young cuckoo)

   (d) (Reciprocal altruism is) providing help to another and being repaid later but in this case there is no repayment to the host.
   or Altruism has costs to one that improve survival of another (as here) but reciprocal altruism would require both partners to benefit
   or Reciprocal altruism has costs to both but here no cost to cuckoo.

4. *Any five from:*
1. Define as (rapid) identification/attachment with another individual/object
2. During narrow time period/in critical period
3. Occurs after birth/hatching
4. Results in following one individual to the exclusion of others
5. Is a learning process/not innate/has environmental component
6. Difficult to reverse/irreversible
7. Adaptive significance/benefit in terms of protection of young/finding food
8. Adaptive significance/benefit in terms of sexual behaviour

Physiology, Health and Exercise

1. (*a*) *Any two from:*
Blood glucose level is higher after fasting/at the start.
Blood glucose level is elevated throughout the test period/longer.
For B the BGL rises faster.
Maximum value reached later in the test period.
Higher maximum value.

(*b*) Glucagon leads to a breakdown of glycogen to increase glucose

(*c*) (i) Being overweight/obesity
(ii) *Any two from:*
Increased sensitivity to insulin
Increase in the number of (active) insulin receptors (on the cell membrane)
Increased blood flow to muscle
Exercise reduces body weight/fat
Exercise increases metabolism
Increase in enzyme activity for glucose storage

2. (*a*) BMR = $0.062 \times 75 + 2.036 = $ **6·686** MJ/day/6·69/6·7

(*b*) (In indirect calorimetry, oxygen consumption is) used in a mathematical formula/calculation/work out the energy released.
or (indirect calorimetry) assumes a relationship between oxygen consumption and energy expenditure.
or direct calorimetry measures the heat produced.

(*c*) *Any five from:*
1. **Body size/mass/weight** - heavier people have a greater BMR (because they have more tissues)
2. **Body composition** - the more lean tissue a person has/more muscular the higher the BMR
3. **Age** - BMR falls with age **or** children have a higher BMR weight for weight than adults
4. **Sex** - BMR higher in males
because they have more lean/muscle tissue
females tend to have more body fat/adipose tissue
5. **Nutritional status (diet)** - BMR reduced by low energy intake/fasting/dieting
6. Because lean tissue is more active metabolically (per kg) than adipose *[applied to either 2, 4 or 5]*
7. Age effect is due to changing body composition
or due to decrease in activity per kg of body tissue
or due to energy cost of growing/since children are actively growing.

3. (*a*) (i) (Maximum) oxygen uptake and body mass
(ii) Maximum stroke volume and maximum heart rate

(*b*) Left ventricular mass has increased (to 300g)

(*c*) Record heart rate with graded exercise and extrapolate to theoretical max HR

or interpolate theoretical max HR on graph of HR against oxygen uptake

4. (*a*) *Any two from:*
diet
smoking
activity level
obesity
stress

(*b*) 110 (mm Hg)

BIOLOGY ADVANCED HIGHER 2008

SECTION A

1.	C	14.	A
2.	D	15.	D
3.	C	16.	D
4.	D	17.	C
5.	B	18.	A
6.	A	19.	A
7.	D	20.	B
8.	A	21.	C
9.	B	22.	B
10.	A	23.	B
11.	B	24.	A
12.	D	25.	C
13.	A		

SECTION B

1. (a) (i) integral/intrinsic
   (ii) quaternary has sub-units **and** aquaporin has four

   (b) (i) so direction/movement can be traced/ tracked/determined
   or can tell which/how many water molecules came from inside
   (ii) (in isotonic conditions) water molecules will move inwards and at equal volume/rate
   (iii) kinase
   (iv) 1·8 to 20 **or** 18·2 increase (in hypertonic) $18·2/1·8 \times 100 = \mathbf{1011}\%$

   (c) (i) significant difference between NN(Nn) and nn for loss
   or nn loses 14% more than NN(Nn)
   NN has AQP1 **and** nn doesn't
   or (in the absence of AQP-1) nn unable to reabsorb as much as NN (in descending limb)
   (ii) (when dehydrated) Nn loses same **mass** as NN (21 to 22%) (Fig 3)
   Increase/change in urine concentration is the same/1700 in both NN and Nn
   Reference to error bars overlapping **or** differences not significant

   (d) (i) NDI people will have higher urine output/more dilute urine
   or NDI people will have unchanged urine output following water shortage
   (ii) (normal 70% reabsorption in the descending limb through AQP1 but) no/less reabsorption in collecting duct because AQP2 non-functioning/AQP2 does not reabsorb water/lack of sensitivity to ADH

2. (a) (i) Nucleosome
   (ii) *Any two from:*
   DNA negatively charged + protein positively charged
   or protein neutralises DNA charge
   Compact 'storage' (of DNA) leads to chromosome formation/essential for mitosis

   (b) (i) *Agrobacterium (tumefaciens)/A. tumefaciens*
   (ii) cellulase and digest cell wall/cellulose

3. 1. four rings **or** correct shape drawn
   And any three from:
   2. variation in side groups in different steroids
   3. hydrophobic/non-polar/lipid-soluble **and** can diffuse/pass/travel through plasma membrane/into cell
   4. bind to proteins/ in cytoplasm/nucleus
   5. (protein complex) regulates genes **or** switches on gene (transcription)
   6. (steroid) hormones (are signalling molecules) eg testosterone

4. (a) Enzyme/active site changes shape **when substrate binds** (to improve the fit)
   (b) it has sites away from the active site where inhibitors/activators/modulators can bind
   (c) AMP inhibits the enzyme **or** AMP exhibits (end-)product inhibition so there is less PRPP/ intermediates **or** the production of AMP decreases **or** AMP 'causes' negative feedback

5. (a) $(175/13000) \times 100 = 1·3\%$

   (b) 70 kJ m^{-2} day^{-1}

   (c) (Eco efficiency for) P/1 is $12/175 = 6·9\%$

   or

   (Eco efficiency for) 1/2 is $2/12 = 16·7\%$

   (d) Heat

   (e) Decomposers external and detritivores internal enzyme digestion

6. (a) Must have oxygen (to carry out metabolism/ respiration)
   or Can only grow in the presence of oxygen.

   (b) (i) *Rhizobium* (in legumes)
   (ii) Nitrogenase
   (iii) Absorbs/binds oxygen to create anaerobic conditions
   or prevents enzyme being inhibited by oxygen
   or prevents oxygen reaching the enzyme

   (c) no effect/no loss/remains the same (since nitrate conversion to N gas/denitrification is anaerobic)

7. (a) Cultivation/growing of single species/crop (over large area).

   (b) If plants are at least **1·25m**/more than **1·25m** apart (no new pustules are formed)

   (c) Fungicide/pesticide
   Selective breeding for resistant varieties
   Genetic engineering/transgenic plants to get resistant varieties

8. (a) (i) Phosphate enrichment:
   Any five from:
   1. Phosphate is a limiting factor in (aquatic) ecosystems
   2. Eutrophication as phosphate/nutrient enrichment
   3. Appropriate source; fertilisers/leachate/ sewage etc.
   4. Algal bloom/algal population explosion mentioned
   5. Growth unsustainable/death of algae occurs **or** less light for plants below
   6. Bacterial decomposition of dead algae /plants **or** toxin production
   7. Oxygen depletion as consequence of bacterial action
   8. Loss of diversity/death of aquatic organisms
   (ii) Exotic species:
   Any four from:
   9. Defined as foreign/introduced/alien species
   10. Example(s)
   11. Reason for success
   12. Description of damaging effect

(iii) Persistent toxic pollutants:

Any six from:

13. Definition of pollution as discharge of harmful substances
14. Example; eg heavy metals/DDT
15. Origin of pollutant, eg industry/ agriculture
16. Non-biodegradable nature/persistence explained
17. Bioaccumulation = build up in single trophic level
18. Biological magnification defined as build up in successive trophic levels
19. Consequences show up at higher trophic levels
20. Effect described; eg eggshell thinning/reduced disease resistance/death of top predators

8. (b) (i) Dormancy:

Any seven from:

1. Period of suspended/reduced activity
   or reduction in metabolism
2. Means of resisting/tolerating/ surviving/avoiding adverse conditions
3. Predictive anticipates/before onset of conditions
4. Consequential is in response to/after onset of conditions
5. Resting spores/seeds are structures that germinate when suitable conditions return
6. Diapause - suspended development in insects
7. Hibernation referring to energy conservation/reduction in body temperature in cold period
8. Aestivation is response to high T/drought
9. Named example in context

(ii) Mimicry:

Any four from:

10. Batesian where palatable/harmless species resembles a harmful one
11. Relative numbers – mimics lower than model
12. Mullerian where harmful species resemble each other
13. Example of either type of mimicry; coral snake – false coral; monarch and viceroy butterflies
14. Reference to aposematic/warning coloration
15. Survival value = defence against predation

(iii) Mutualism:

Any four from:

16. Mutualism is a form of symbiosis
17. Mutualism is close/intimate/long-term relationship
18. Relationship in which both **species** benefit
19. Name of two species involved
20. Description of mutual benefits

SECTION C

Biotechnology

1. (a) *Any two from:*
   1. small number of cells to start with/for division
   2. period of adaptation/adjustment
   3. some cells may be depleted of essential growth metabolites/substances/may need to absorb nutrients
   4. cells undergoing repair (due to damage during storage)
   5. essential enzymes are being induced/ change takes place in cells

   (b) (i) overlapping cells are only included in the count once
   or if included overlapping cells lead to overestimate

   (ii) volume over grid = $0.2 \times 0.2 \times 0.1$
   count is 20 cells, so 1 mm^3 contains 20/0.004
   = **5000** cells

(c) (i) bacteriostatic – inhibitory/cells arrested, not dead **or** regrow when diluted
bactericidal – lethal/kills

(ii) Streptomycin/tetracycline/erythromycin etc.

(d) (i) B lymphocytes

(ii) Diagnostic testing/ diagnosis of disease
Elisa
Treatment of disease (eg rabies, breast cancer)

2. *Any four from:*
   1. polygalacturonase breaks down pectin
   2. which causes fruit to soften
      or modification/treatment slows down ripening/bruising
   3. gene for enzyme is cloned
   4. gene inserted into plant genome in reverse/antisense technology idea
   5. mRNA strand from inserted gene is complementary to mRNA for enzyme
      or sense and antisense mRNAs bind
   6. gene silenced/translation prevented
   7. enzyme not made/reduced enzyme level

3. (a) (i) Trend: as proportion of BK1 increases biomass increases
   + any one correct quantification

   (ii) higher nitrogen content of BK1 or more amino acids available for growth

   (b) Starter for silage **or** for silage production

4. (a) breakdown of yeast cells by their own enzymes

   (b) *Any two from:*
   stage of life cycle
   age of yeast culture
   yeast strain
   pre-treatment of yeast cells with enzymes
   mechanical disruption of yeast cell wall
   pH
   temperature
   enzymes produced by yeast due to genetic makeup

   (c) source of vitamins (as in Marmite)
   flavourings (of soups/gravies/sauces/foods with non animal origin)

Animal Behaviour

1. (a) Female choice
   or advantage following female preference, eg advantage from size through genes **or** burrowing **or** survival
   or
   Male-male rivalry
   or
   Competitive advantage arising from size eg access to more females

   (b) Proximate: to avoid drying out/heat/environmental conditions
   Ultimate: increased breeding success/survival of genes

   (c) Female: greater energy/costs because of bigger gametes/incubation of eggs/carrying young in pouch
   or converse for males

   (d) Genetically determined/stereotyped/instinctive

   (e) Reduced

2. (a) (Natural selection favouring) behaviour that increases relative's survival/fitness

(b) (Those without B have) no receptors/protein **and** either cannot identify intruder ants **or** don't distinguish other colony members from their own so not aggressive to intruders
or don't maintain loyalty to their queen

(c) *Drosophila per* gene/hygienic behaviour in bees

3. *Any four from:*
   1. High levels of homozygosity in inbred populations
   2. Heterozygosity in outbred populations
   3. Inbreeding increases expression of disadvantageous/ lethal recessive genes **or** converse for outbreeding
   4. Inbreeding results in lower fitness/inbreeding depression/reduced breeding success **or** converse for outbreeding
   5. Male dispersal in mammals/or example
   6. Female dispersal in birds/or example

4. (a) (i) 1 year versus 3/4/adult,
           2 year versus 4/adult
           3 year versus adult
       (ii) increasing feeding rate as they get older **because** they learn what is edible/compete better/feed more efficiently
       (iii) 300 s
             or
             298·8/299
   (b) Allow (more) accurate recording (of age/feeding rate)**or** reduces errors
       Watch again to check/ensure accuracy
       Observer does not affect behaviour
   (c) Changes in:
       diet/or example **or** foraging behaviour/or example habitat preference/or eg **or** nesting behaviour

Physiology, Health and Exercise

1. (a) Coronary arteries/coronary blood vessels
   (b) Build up of plaque/atheroma in vessel wall
       Composition of atheroma: fatty material/ cholesterol/fibrous material/smooth muscle cells/calcium loss of elasticity/hardening of vessel walls (increasing BP)/LDL transport of cholesterol for deposition
   (c) (i) Lumen volume increases (so increased blood flow)
             Quantification: doubles lumen volume/65 to 129-133 mm^3
             or Atheroma decrease is 15 mm^3
       (ii) Angina/Angina pectoris

2. (a) Bones become (more) porous/brittle
       or reference to spine curvature
   (b) More common in women with low/reduced oestrogen/in menopausal or post-menopausal women
   (c) (i) The **number** of women with osteoporosis is increasing (from 7·8 to 10·5 million)
       (ii) The **percentage/proportion** of women with low bone mass who go on to develop osteoporosis is decreasing (35·7% to 34·5%.)(ratio 2·8:1 to 2·9:1)
   (d) Jogging is weight-bearing exercise **or** swimming is not
       Jogging/regular weight-bearing exercise maintains/ increases/promotes bone mass/ strength/density **or**
       Jogging when younger maximizes bone density before age-related loss

3. (a) (i) $(10 \times 29\cdot4)/3 = $ **98** (days)
       (ii) $96/(1\cdot74 \times 1\cdot74) = $ **31·7**

   (b) Increased body mass may be due to a large muscle mass or bone mass **and**
       High lean: fat is healthier/muscle accumulation healthy
       or high fat: lean unhealthy/fat accumulation is unhealthy

(c) Densitometry/skinfold thickness/bioelectric impedance analysis /waist to hip ratio/mid-upper arm circumference.

4. 1. Testing can be maximal or sub-maximal
   2. Sub-maximal testing used to monitor/improve aerobic fitness of cardiac patients/less fit
   3. Maximal testing measures maximal oxygen uptake/$VO_{2\,max}$ in athletes/fit people
   4. Sub-maximal tests are predictive/estimates of $VO_{2\,max}$
   5. Predictive/sub-maximal tests assume a linear relationship between heart rate and O_2 consumption/exercise intensity
   6. Description of exercise stress test(s) used: step test/shuttle test/treadmill **or** Maximal tests to exhaustion

BIOLOGY ADVANCED HIGHER 2009

SECTION A

1.	A	14.	A
2.	B	15.	D
3.	B	16.	C
4.	D	17.	B
5.	B	18.	D
6.	A	19.	A
7.	C	20.	C
8.	D	21.	B
9.	C	22.	A
10.	A	23.	C
11.	D	24.	B
12.	C	25.	D
13.	B		

SECTION B

1. (a) An organism that consumes complex/organic molecules
   or consumer
   or feeds on/gets energy from other organisms

   (b) (i) Wolves cause (herbivores decrease) aspen increase
      wolf **increase** data (dates or numbers)
      and corresponding aspen data (damage decrease or height increase)
      (ii) 208%
      (iii) *Any one from*:
      • high reproduction rate of elk
      • elk reproduction replaces predation loss
      • prey consumed were not reproductive
      • (young) wolves eat other animals
      • many wolves are young and not hunting yet
      • more vegetation/food for elk so more survive

   (c) *Any two from*:
      Older trees more (abundant) in Zion Canyon than in N Creek **or** not much difference
      Younger trees **much** more (abundant) in N Creek than in Zion Canyon
      More older trees than young trees in Zion Canyon
      or More younger trees than older trees in North Creek

   (d) *Any one from*:
      • investigators would scare them away/cougars go into hiding (because cougars are sensitive to humans)
      • same cougar may be counted twice
      • sightings not reliable/accurate (so counting scats is better)
      • scats more easily spotted than cougars/static
      • numbers of scats proportional to number of cougars

   (e) In Zion Canyon/where there are tourists, cougars are absent and there are few saplings/cottonwood
      or
      In North Creek/where there is no tourism the cougars are present and there are many saplings/cottonwood
      Tourism started in 1930s (in Zion Canyon) and since then there are few trees

   (f) (i) Density dependent
      (ii) *Any two from*:
      Excessive/high intensity grazing leads to less diversity because all/most/several/some species are killed
      Moderate grazing increases diversity because dominant species are kept in check/others can now grow/rarer species survive better with less competition/those with basal meristems survive etc
      Low intensity grazing reduces diversity because a single species dominates/outcompetes the others

2. (a) (i) Resisting/tolerating/surviving environmental adversity
      (ii) *Any one from*:
      • reduction in population of native species
      • extinction
      • reduction in biodiversity
      • competitive exclusion
      • loss of habitat
      • spread of disease to native plants
      (iii) Herbicide/pesticide/cutting/removal/disease/herbivore
      (iv) Need to control for 2 or so years to allow dormant seeds to germinate
      or
      Cut down/spray plants before flowering for two years
      or
      Remove/kill all dormant seeds after vegetation removed

   (b) Reduction in soil quality/erosion/compaction
      Reduction humus/nutrients/fertility

3. 1. CO_2 from burning/use of fossil fuels
   2. **enhanced** greenhouse effect
   3. causes global warming
   4. <u>zooxanthellae</u> and coral (symbiosis) is mutualistic
   5. as sea temperature increases algae leave the coral
   6. coral bleaching

4. (a) Harmful for both species/organisms involved (in interaction)

   (b) Resources a species is capable of using in **the absence of competition**

   (c) *Any two from*:
      No two species with same niche can coexist
      Interspecific competition is intense (because both species have similar fundamental niche)
      Competitive exclusion has occurred **or** description of **local** extinction of one of the species

   (d) (i) Co-evolution of **host and parasite**
      or
      Specificity of **host and parasite**
      (ii) (Direct) contact/vector/resistant stage/secondary host/vertical

5. (a) (i) B, C, D, E
      (ii) Hydrophilic
      <u>Peptide</u> hormone
      Neurotransmitter

   (b) (i) Four ring structure (with variable groups attached)
      (ii) (Affects) fluidity/permeability (of membrane/phospholipid bilayer)
      (iii) 6:1:2

6. (a) (Repressor binding to the operator switches) structural gene off/not transcribed/not expressed
      or
      no beta galactosidase/lactase/lactose-digesting enzyme made

   (b) (i) Secondary
      (ii) Basic
      (iii) Positive charges (of lysine) interact/bond with/attracted to the negative charges on DNA

7. (a) $50\mu MI^{-1}$ (micromoles per litre); 51 OK

   (b) (Competitive) inhibitor occupies active site **and** a higher concentration of/more substrate is needed to reach (half) V_{max}/same rate of reaction

   (c) 5×10^{-4}s or other formats

8. A   1. glucose exists in linear and ring forms
2. more of the ring form
3. description of C1 OH group in α position below plane/ring and β above plane/ring
4. glucose monomers join by condensation reaction/glycosidic bonds
5. diagram of alpha (1,4) bond **or** beta (1,4) bond **or** alpha (1,6) bond
6. (side) branches are between C1 and C6
7. starch is found in plants **and** function is **energy** storage
8. two forms of starch - amylose and amylopectin
9. starch has glucose monomers joined by α (1,4) bonds
10. amylose linear/has no (side) branches
11. amylose forms a helix
12. glycogen is found in animals **and** function is **energy** storage
13. glycogen has glucose monomers joined by α (1,4) bonds
14. amylopectin has less branching than glycogen
15. cellulose is found in plants **and** provides support/is structural
16. cellulose has glucose monomers joined by β (1,4) bonds
17. cellulose has glucose molecules inverted every second molecule
18. gives a rigid/straight chain
19. chains form fibrils
20. starch and glycogen are insoluble **and** do not affect osmosis

B   1. PCR is used to **amplify** DNA
2. DNA denatured/melted by heating to about 90°C
3. cooled to let primers anneal/attach
4. primers are short base sequence complementary to sample
5. primers delimit the copy region
6. Taq polymerase optimum temperature about 70°C
   or
   Taq polymerase stable at high temperature
7. polymerase synthesises complementary strand
8. cycle repeated 30 or so/many times
9. used for forensics/paternity disputes/testing pedigrees
10. DNA samples are isolated/purified
11. samples digested with restriction enzyme/endonuclease
12. differences between individuals' genomes
    or
    reference to hypervariable repeat sequences/VNTR
13. fragment lengths of digested DNA vary between individuals
14. fragments separated by electrophoresis
15. electric current/electricity passed through gel
16. DNA has a negative charge/phosphates charged
17. shorter fragments travel further/faster
18. fragments blotted onto a filter/membrane
19. probe is a short chain of single stranded DNA
20. probe binds to complementary bases on fragments/hybridisation occurs
21. fragments with probe attached show up
    or probe is labelled
22. Correct description of outcome

SECTION C: BIOTECHNOLOGY

1. (*a*) (i) ELISA/immunoassay
    (ii) Antibodies are specific to antigens
       or
       HSV antigens/epitopes not the same as those for chickenpox
    (iii) Some antibody R-enzyme would be present and react with substrate
       even though it is not bound to Q

       or even though no Q is present
       or even if some Q is present but unattached (to HSV antigen)

    (*b*) Myeloma and (B) lymphocyte/B-cells

2. (*a*) (i) Lactose to lactic acid
    (ii) Pasteurisation
       or
       to kill pathogens/naturally occurring bacteria/spoilage bacteria

    (*b*) (i) Two species present/two different types of cell present
      (ii) *Any one from*:
       • culture has become contaminated
       • pasteurisation process not successful
       • two bacterial species in added culture

3. *Any 5 points from:*
1. single colony from an agar plate
2. transfer to (nutrient) broth /liquid culture
3. purity/(stage of) growth checked by plating on agar/by microscopy
4. succession of transfers to increasing volumes
5. fermenters for larger volumes
6. and 7. Any two factors for consideration in scaling up
    • cost
    • containment of micro-organisms
    • aseptic transfers
    • sterilisation of fermenters
    • abiotic – pH/temperature/oxygen/stirring

4. (*a*) Silo (tower)/bunker/pit

    (*b*) Creates anaerobic conditions (which leads to) **and** lowered pH/acidic conditions/lactic acid **Spoilage** organisms do not grow/are killed

    (*c*) *Enterococcus (faecalis)/Lactobacillus (plantarum)*

    (*d*) (i) Lower free amino acids indicates less protein breakdown
      (ii) (Added bacteria have) no **significant** effect on lactic acid content
       or
       If using lactic acid conclusion in d(i) then accept **Significantly** lower free amino acids indicates less protein protein breakdown

SECTION C: ANIMAL BEHAVIOUR

1. (*a*) (i) (Although) Stages 2 and 5 (approx) 25% abundance
      or proportion similar
      (Birds made) 75% (approx) of foraging choices for stage 2 flowers (0% for stage 5)
    (ii) maximising <u>energy</u> gain **and** minimising expenditure
      or maximum **net** gain in <u>energy</u>
    (iii) Stage 2 flowers have greatest availability of nectar **and** these are visited most frequently
      or
      As nectar production increases foraging increases

    (*b*) (i) (Energy) cost of gamete production is greater in females
      (ii) Genes for nest building have effects outside the body of the bird

    (*c*) Similar/the same

2. (*a*) (i) Most rapid response is (to silk from) unmated females
    (ii) Latency
    (iii) Frequency/duration/intensity/strength
    (iv) Behaviour may differ from that shown in the wild
      Other factors/stimuli from natural habitat not present
      Investigator influences behaviour

(b) Prevent/reduce chances of being eaten by females

or

Prevent waste of time/energy in courting unreceptive female/increased chance of mating

3. (a) *Any one from*:
- larger proportion/more likely to be on outside of groups **and** more vulnerable/easier to catch
- more spaced out/further away from neighbours **and** more vulnerable/easier to catch
- spend less time scanning **and** less likely to detect cheetah

(b) 18

(c) Vigilance

4. 1. agonistic behaviour - all aspects of competitive/fighting behaviour
2. threat/attack to establish dominance/status (in a social group)
3. appeasement/submissive behaviour terminates attack/inhibits aggression
4. example of appeasement/submissive posture eg sexual presentation in baboons
5. ritualised display allows assessment of opponent/chances of success
6. (ritualised display) reduces energy expenditure/reduces fighting or risk of injury
7. example of ritualised display eg roaring/parallel walk in red deer
8. reduced risk of predation in social group (benefit all group membership)
9. increased chance of all individuals/subordinates obtaining food

SECTION C: PHYSIOLOGY, HEALTH AND EXERCISE

1. (a) (i) Weight and height
    (ii) 25 – 34
    (iii) Obesity increases with age
    (iv) Hypertension, (C)HD, diabetes (type 2/NIDDM)

(b) (i) Fat-free mass/lean tissue/muscle conducts electricity

or

Fat offers resistance/impedes current

The higher the impedance/the lower the current **and** the higher the % fat

(ii) Depends on hydration/kidney function

Overestimates fat in lean people or underestimates fat in obese people

2. 1. cardiac output (CO) increases
2. to keep up with demand for oxygen
3. heart rate and stroke volume increase

or

equation CO = HR × SV
4. CO/SV increase from greater distension of ventricle

or CO/HR/SV increase from adrenalin

or CO/HR increase by sympathetic nerves/stimulation
5. force of contraction/systolic BP/BP increases
6. general point about redistribution of blood to muscles

or example of redistribution **from choices below**
- increased blood flow/vasodilation in skeletal muscle
- increased blood flow to heart muscle/through coronary arteries
- increased blood flow/vasodilation in skin
- reduced blood flow/vasoconstriction in viscera

3. (a) *Any 2 from*:

Exercising muscles need oxygen for energy release/ATP production/aerobic respiration

The rate that muscles work at depends on the ability to deliver oxygen to them

Higher VO_{2max} indicates higher oxygen consumption/higher fitness

(b) (The fitness value is) derived by dividing O_2 uptake by body mass

or it is **per kg** tissue

or quantify using eg dividing max O_2 by body mass

(c) **2.896** or **2.9** l min^{-1}

(d) Patient recovering from MI or heart condition

Elderly

4. (a) Thermic effect of food/dietary (induced) thermogenesis

(b) *Any one from*:

Either sugar increases energy expenditure

(Energy expenditure) for sucrose more than glucose

Different sugars give different changes in EE

(c) *Any one from*:
- difference between sugars is not due to chance/biological variation
- significant difference between glucose and sucrose results
- obtained by testing a number of individuals
- glucose results more reliable
- results are mean values
- there is variation between individuals

(d) Direct – measures heat output **and** indirect – measures oxygen uptake etc

BIOLOGY ADVANCED HIGHER 2010

SECTION A

1. C	14. C
2. D	15. B
3. C	16. D
4. A	17. B
5. A	18. B
6. C	19. D
7. B	20. C
8. C	21. D
9. A	22. D
10. B	23. A
11. D	24. B
12. D	25. B
13. A	

SECTION B

1. (a) it/oncogene is **dominant**
   the mutation/mutated allele is dominant
   mutated proto-oncogene/mutated proliferation gene are dominant

   (b) (i) monolayer/one layer/single layer
   confluent/**complete** coverage
   (ii) stimulates cell proliferation/division
   or
   provides/is a source of growth factors/MPF

   (c) (i) the two genes/*EML4* and *ALK* alone/not fused/do not transform cells/produce foci
   (ii) modification of fusion (gene) stops foci formation/transformation
   modification removes kinase activity

   (d) (At zero inhibitor conc. in Fig 2 and Fig 3)
   both normal and transformed cells start at 10^6 cells and both reach 10^{10} cells by day 7

   (e) (i) (at day 7, cell number) in absence of inhibitor is 10^{10} and 10^8 in presence of inhibitor **and** difference of x10^2
   (ii) *Any one from:*
   • as concentration of inhibitor increases, (rate of) growth/proliferation decreases
   • inhibitor reduces growth more in transformed cells than normal cells
   • both 5 µmol l^{-1} and 10 µmol l^{-1} inhibitor reduce cell **number** relative to 0 µmol l^{-1}
   (iii) comparison of final cell numbers **or** of numbers at a specified period/time from both graphs

   (f) *Any one from:*
   This is the concentration that:
   • made transformed cells decrease
   • was effective at killing transformed cells
   • reduced transformed cell number to 10^2
   • would reduce tumour size
   very little effect on normal cells

2. (a) peptidoglycan

   (b) (i) C1 (of NAM) bonded to C4 (of NAG)
   OH of C1 is above plane/ring/carbon
   (ii) hydrolysis

3. *Any five from:*
   1. protein that spans the membrane
   2. works against concentration gradient/by active transport
   3. ATP provides phosphate
   4. phosphate attaches to pump/protein/protein phosphorylated
   5. phosphorylation/dephosphorylation alters conformation/shape of protein **or** description
   6. different conformations have different affinity for sodium/potassium
   7. (3) sodium ions (pumped) out of cell and (2) potassium in

4. (a) contains foreign DNA **or** contains DNA from another **species**

   (b) *Agrobacterium (tumefaciens)/A. tumefaciens*

   (c) selects for plants/cells with the plasmid/resistance gene **or** is toxic to (plant) cells with no plasmid/resistance gene surviving (plant) cells now have the desirable/transgene sequence

   (d) bacterial toxin/Bt toxin/insecticide in tomato/other plants
   herbicide resistance added to in corn/maize/cotton/other plants
   beta carotene added to/in rice
   increased shelf life (flavr savr) tomato

5. (a) (In intraspecific, individuals are from the same species so) individuals have the same resource needs/niche
   or
   converse for interspecific

   (b) (i) B
   (ii) any competition is negative
   or
   presence of any competitor reduces time spent feeding/at flower
   or
   interspecific more intense than **intra**specific

   (c) butterfly has other food/nectar sources
   or
   brambles pollinated by other insects /nectar eaten by other insects
   or
   idea that relationship is not intimate/fixed/symbiotic

6. (a) herbivores eat plants **and** detritivores eat dead/waste material

   (b) (i) comparison of sample 1 and sample 4
   at week 6:
   Sample 1: 11-12 % loss (88% remaining)
   Sample 4: 90% loss (10% remaining)
   or
   compare data from sample 1 and sample 4
   sample 1 has 85% left at 12 weeks and sample 4 reached 85% remaining by week 1 (roughly). So rate of decomposition is 12 times faster = > 7

   Single mark options
   If not comparing Samples 1 and 4 but data show >7
   or
   losses calculated for Samples other than 1 and 4
   (ii) error bars/results overlap **and** no difference in results for types of gut/amount of decomposition
   or
   no **significant** difference
   or
   wide error bars so results very variable/are less reliable
   (iii) material has been through two animal guts **and** idea that fragmentation/surface area increasing (so this sample has the highest rate of decomposition)

7. (a) with pollution there are favoured and susceptible species

indicator species defined as those that experience consequences/are sensitive to a pollutant

or

example showing **how** a favoured/susceptible species indicates pollution

(b) (i) 11 000 000

(ii) not enough time for diclofenac to reach safe levels or equivalent

8. **A** (i) *Any seven from:*

1. yield reduced by competition/disease/ damage/herbivores
2. (any of above) controlled by reducing populations (to maximise food production)
3. weeds are competitors for the crop's resources
4. herbicides used to kill other plants/weeds
5. alternative methods of reducing weeds, e.g. hoeing, interplanting, (herbicide-tolerant) transgenics
6. more resources for the crop (increases yield)
   or e.g. of resource – nitrate, light, space
7. insects (damage crops by) eating plant parts
8. insecticides reduce insect populations/kill insects
   or (Bt) transgenic **or** biological control **or** barrier
9. herbivores removed or kept out (e.g. scarers, netting, fencing)
10. parasites/fungi/viruses reduce yield by causing disease
11. fungicides prevent/kill fungi
12. example of ecological impact of these activities

(ii) *Any eight from:*

13. cultivation of one species/crop (to exclusion of others)
14. to meet the demand/needs of increasing population
15. removal of hedgerows allows increased field size
16. reduces species diversity (e.g. predators)
17. reduces stability of ecosystem
    or increases susceptibility to pathogens
18. mechanisation increases efficiency of cropping/planting
19. reduce food costs/increases profit
20. may damage soil structure/increase compaction
    or may have negative impact on soil condition
21. cultivation of single species depletes particular nutrients
22. need for fertiliser/use of inorganic fertiliser (improves yield)
23. but can cause knock on pollution problems/eg of effect

8. **B** (i) *Any five from:*

1. energy fixed/light to chemical in photosynthesis
2. (photosynthesis carried out) by autotrophs/producers
3. productivity is **rate** of accumulation of biomass
   or productivity is mass units per area per time
4. primary productivity supports higher trophic levels
5. GPP is total yield of organic matter / total energy fixed
6. NPP is biomass remaining after producer respiration
   or equation
7. appropriate management/choice of biomass crop
8. explanation of role of biomass in the energy debate
   or relevant comment about 'carbon footprint'/neutrality

(ii) *Any ten from:*

9. fossil fuels are finite/non-renewable (energy) resources
10. need to be conserved

11. biofuels are alternative sources of energy
12. fossil fuels are **burned**
13. gases released SO_2/ NOx/ CO_2
14. these cause acid rain
15. effect of acid rain in ecosystems (e.g. forest damage, pH in lakes, etc)
16. CO_2 (from combustion) **enhances** greenhouse effect
17. cause global warming/climate change
18. changes abundance or distribution of species (general point)
    or example **other than** zooxanthellae
19. zooxanthellae and polyps/coral are symbiotic/mutualistic
20. and coral bleaching link to temperature rise
21. methane and CFCs other important greenhouse gases not from fossil fuels

Section C: Biotechnology

1. (a) (i) nif/nitrogen-fixing genes

(ii) nitrogen converted to ammonia/ammonium

(b) *Any two from:*

nitrogenase activity declines with length of treatment

no significant difference between 10 and 20 days

there is a (significant) decrease in activity from 20 to 30 days

2. *Response to antigens*

1. antigens are recognised by B-lymphocytes
   or antigens activate B-lymphocytes
2. multiplication (of B-lymphocytes) in spleen/immune system
3. antibodies are produced
4. antibody binds/forms complex with antigen
   or antibodies are specific

Application

5. (highly purified) antigen injected into animal
6. bleeding of animal
   or red blood cells removed from blood sample
7. reinjection (with antigen) increases response
8. polyclonal serum produced **or** antibodies prepared from serum

3. (a) *Any one from:*

Uniformity in terms of:
- clones/genetic
- growth rate
- ripening
- harvesting time
- yields
- taste

high yielding disease free/virus free/economical

(b) light intensity/temperature/humidity/ nutrients/pH/water content

(c) (i) treatments are an improvement on the control **or** example

or

as concentration of regulators increase the explants increase

(ii) (At 0·5 IAA + 5·0 kinetin)
$58 \times 28 = 1624$ shoots = highest yield

4. (a) competition with gut pathogens **or** control pathogens **or** reduce diarrhoea

anti-cancer activity

reduction of blood cholesterol

reduced lactose intolerance

(b) (i) direct count would include living and dead

    or dilution plating gives viable count

    or alternative comparisons, eg **live** bacteria needed so need **viable** count

(ii) prevent contamination/maintain aseptic technique

(iii) only count between 30 and 300

    or

    enough to be accurate and not too many to count

(iv) correct value 6×10^{10}

    plate to bottle $4 = 6 \times 10^{3}$

    dilution factor from bottle 1 to bottle $4 = \mathbf{10^{4}}$ $(10^{2} \times 10 \times 10)$

    scaling $0 \cdot 1$ cm^3 sample from 100 cm^3 in carton $= 10^{3}$

Plate —————————> bottles —————————> carton
60 in $0.1 \times 100 = 6000$ $\times 10 \times 10 \times 100$ $\times 1000$

Section C: Animal Behaviour

1. (a) background/height/tree species/type of woodland etc

(b) B or E

(c) (B was expected to give best survival but)
Little difference between B and C
or C is effective yet has only one spot/has 'no eyes'
(E with two 'eyes' was expected to give high survival but)
Increase in number of spots increases survival
F–E–D (24/48 hrs)
(A, the control has no contrast and)
In all treatments survival is higher than control
B–C–D have highest contrast and highest survival
Appropriate quantification

(d) mimicry/batesian mimicry/mullerian mimicry
crypsis/camouflage
masquerade
disruptive coloration
aposematic/warning coloration

2. *Any four from:*
1. hierarchy is system of (social) ranking
2. established by fighting/maintained by threat or ritualised display
3. reduced aggression/fighting (once established)
4. increased protection/better chance of survival
5. co-operative hunting/all group members get food
6. division of labour/opportunities for learning

3. (a) ethogram

(b) (i) sexual dimorphism

(ii) to attract females/to permit female choice/to elicit response from females

(c) (i) brother-sister matings

    or

    mating (only) between closely related fish

    or Prevent dispersal/keep all family individuals in the same area

(ii) reduces breeding success **or** less fertilisation and less hatching
Inbreeding causes:
increased expression of disadvantageous/lethal/ recessive genes
increased homozygosity/inbreeding depression

4. (a) (i) high-learning flies die younger/shorter life span

(ii) (on average/in either group) females live longer than males

    or

    greater reduction in life span/longevity for females (in high-learning group)

(iii) much longer life span in primates

    or

    learning has bigger role in primate behaviour

    or

    learning benefits outweigh the costs in primates

(b) *Any two from:*
irreversible/difficult to reverse
environmental component/object in environment
critical time period (after hatching/birth)
object (of attachment) followed to exclusion of others

Section C: Physiology, Health and Exercise

1. (a) *Any two from:*
3+ hours/endurance level of exercise results in lower (resting) heart/pulse rate than **the others**

3+ hours/endurance level of exercise results in greater left ventricle mass than **the others**

athletic heart defined as increased LV thickness **and** increased SV/lower (resting) pulse

(b) stroke volume

(c) increased LV mass

(d) less plaque/atheroma build up/atherosclerosis
better lipid profile/higher HDL:LDL ratio/higher HDL/lower LDL
better myocardial circulation
lower (resting) BP
lowers risk of MI/stroke

2. *Any five from:*
1. pancreas senses glucose (in blood)
2. insulin secretion/production (increases) when glucose is high
3. insulin increases glucose uptake by liver/muscle/cells
4. insulin **promotes** glycogen synthesis/conversion of glucose to glycogen
5. insulin increases the number of glucose transporters (in cell membranes)
6. obesity leads to/is a risk factor for NIDDM (Type 2 diabetes)
7. obesity/NIDDM leads to insulin resistance/loss of sensitivity to insulin/fewer **active** receptors
8. reduced entry of glucose into cells
9. (in NIDDM) insulin concentration initially increases

3. (a) bone mass/density is increasing in this period

    or

    to increase bone density (before age-related loss)

    or

    weight bearing activity is likely to be high

(b) reference to menopause around this age/oestrogen starts to decline/women start to lose bone mass rapidly/when osteoporosis (most likely) starts

may counteract/slow down (age-related/oestrogen-related) losses

    or

    maintain bone density/mass

    or

    delay onset of osteoporosis

4. (a) (i) measures heat output/loss

    in **insulated** chamber/environment
    or measure energy required to keep chamber temperature constant

(ii) volume of air breathed
% oxygen breathed in and % of oxygen in air out
or difference in percentages

(b) (i) 838.3 kJ

(ii) select foods with biggest deviation from $20 \cdot 20$ kJ (starch or protein) correct calculation of either extreme (as fraction of single food value)

starch (low) = 4·62%   protein (high) = 4·87%

or

5% limits from 20.20 are 19·19 kJ to 21·21 kJ
and
conclude all four are in range

or

4 deviations calculated correctly
and
conclude all four are in range

BIOLOGY ADVANCED HIGHER 2011

SECTION A

1.	C	14.	A
2.	B	15.	A
3.	B	16.	C
4.	D	17.	C
5.	D	18.	D
6.	B	19.	C
7.	A	20.	D
8.	A	21.	C
9.	B	22.	B
10.	D	23.	D
11.	D	24.	B
12.	A	25.	B
13.	C		

SECTION B

1. (a) (i) *Any two from:*
Type of symbiosis **or** idea of close/intimate association between two **species**
Host harmed and parasite benefits
Benefit (to parasite) in terms of nutrition/energy/resources
   (ii) Obligate

   (b) (i) Idea of checking human faeces (for parasite eggs)
   (ii) *Any two from:*
Health education/ideas on how to reduce infection
Sanitation/prevent faeces reaching lake
Drug treatment (for superspreaders)

   (c) (i) Intervention village(s) reach target/1% and control(s) don't.
Use data to illustrate trends
   (ii) Commit to position about the results (reliable or unreliable) **and** justify appropriately, eg 'Reliable because two villages used for treatment and control', or 'not reliable because (*only*) *two* villages …' Reliability in relation to **error bars** – when error bars are small the reliability is better

   (d) (i) Difficult to kill them all
or
Survivors reproduce rapidly
   (ii) *Any one from:*
(Parasites still exist as)
Adults long lived/still inside host
Eggs still being produced
Free-living parasite stages not affected

   (e) *S.japonicum* can infect other **mammals**/can have a range of primary hosts
(so) cattle have to be kept away from lake
(and) mice can be used for test purposes

2. (a) photosynthesis **and** respiration

   (b) 12.5%

   (c) (i) added to by human activity
   (ii) methane/CFC/nitrous oxide/ozone

3. (a) (i) earlier species **change conditions/environment** to better suit later species
   (ii) allogenic

   (b) (i) bioaccumulation/bioconcentration
   (ii) high toxicity so herbivores/primary consumers die

or

biomagnification makes herbivores too toxic (for carnivores)/biomagnification results in toxicity in higher trophic levels

or

low productivity/too little energy to support higher levels

    (iii) survives high conc. of nickel while **other species** susceptible

    or

the **relative abundance** depends on Ni levels of soil

4. *Any four from:*

1. Fundamental niche is the resources a species is capable of using/could use in the absence of competition
2. Realised niche is the resources a species actually uses or available in presence of competitors
3. (Competition arises) when resources limited
4. Competitive exclusion arises from interspecific competition/when two **species** competing
5. Two **species** with the same/similar niche cannot coexist (in same location)
6. (One species will survive and) one species will die out/local extinction

5. (*a*) (i) (For the increase in O_2 pressure 0–30 units)

      Myoglobin increases to 0.975

      Haemoglobin increases to 0.50

    (ii) curves differ/binding differs

      tertiary (structure) the same/similar

      only Hb has quaternary

(*b*) 1 (less)

(*c*) prosthetic groups

6. (*a*) (i) hydrophilic/not lipid soluble

    (ii) (signal) transduction

(*b*) (i) at most/all GABA concentrations more chloride movement (with drug present)

    (ii) change in conformation/shape (of the GABA receptor)

7. (*a*) single-stranded DNA

(bases) complementary **or** strand anneals (to template)

(*b*) *Any one from:*

(gene) probes/probing

(gel) electrophoresis

blotting

sequencing

restriction digest

(*c*) (Test is negative for ΔF508 so counselling needs to warn of) other possible mutations (30%) causing CF

or low chance of having/carrying CF

8. A (i) *Any five from:*

Prokaryotic DNA

   1. within cytoplasm/not contained in a nuclear membrane

   2. exists as a circular DNA molecule/nucleoid

   3. plasmids are **additional** circles/rings of DNA

Eukaryotic

   4. contained within a nuclear membrane

   5. DNA is associated with histone/proteins

   6. organised as nucleosomes/chromatin

   7. (nucleosomes) coiled/condensed to form chromosomes

   8. chromosomes are linear

(ii) *Any ten from:*

Prokaryotic

   9. ribosomes (only organelle)

  10. cell wall made of peptidoglycan

  11. capsule/layer of mucus (lipopolysaccharide) is protective/is adhesive

  12. pili for cell attachment/exchanging plasmids

  13. flagella for movement

Eukaryotic

  14. name and function of one organelle from list below

  15. name and function of another organelle from list below

  16. cytoskeleton is a system of protein fibres that provide support **or** movement **or** movement/organisation of organelles

  17. animal cells (may) have microvilli to increase surface area/absorption

  18. plant cell walls made of cellulose

  19. middle lamella is where plant cell walls contact (rich in pectin)

  20. plasmodesmata connect cytoplasms/adjacent plant cells

  21. plant cells (may) also contain – chloroplasts for photosynthesis **or** vacuoles for cell sap

8. B Eukaryotic

Endoplasmic reticulum – transport of proteins/synthesis of lipids

Golgi apparatus – processing/modification/secretion of proteins

Mitochondrion – (aerobic) respiration/ATP production

Lysosomes – enzymatic digestion

Microbodies/peroxisomes – oxidation reactions

Ribosomes – protein synthesis

Nucleolus – ribosome formation

(i) *Any five from:*

   1. interphase is G_1, S, G_2

    or interphase is the period between cell divisions

   2. G_1 and G_2 are growth periods **or** organelles/ proteins made

   3. DNA replication occurs during S phase

   4. G_1 checkpoint assesses cell size/mass

   5. G_1 checkpoint ensures there is sufficient (mass) to make two daughter cells/to enter S phase

   6. G_2 checkpoint assesses DNA replication

   7. G_2 checkpoint controls entry into mitosis

   8. ensuring each daughter cell receives a complete genome/'set' of DNA

(ii) *Any five from:*

   9. spindle fibres are microtubules

  10. correct description of one phase of mitosis – as in notes

  11. as above

  12. M/metaphase checkpoint controls entry to **anaphase**

  13. ensures chromosomes are aligned correctly (on the equator)

    or ensures each daughter cell receives correct number of chromosomes/chromatids

  14. mitosis promoting factor (MPF) needed for entry to mitosis

    or MPF is a protein

  15. cytokinesis is the division of the cytoplasm/separation into two cells

   (iii) *Any five from:*
      16. proto-oncogenes/proliferation genes stimulate cell division
      17. proto-oncogenes mutate to oncogenes
      18. oncogenes stimulate excessive/abnormal cell division/tumour formation
      19. tumour suppressor genes/anti-proliferation genes inhibit cell division
      20. tumour suppressors act at checkpoints
      21. (tumour suppressor) mutation results in loss of inhibition/loss of control of division
      22. oncogenes are dominant and in tumour suppressor genes, mutations are recessive
         or
         only single oncogene mutation required whereas two tumour suppressor mutations required

Section C: Biotechnology

1. (a) Antibiotic **and** type of organism
      e.g. penicillin and *Penicillium*/fungus
      or
      Correct antibiotic and *Streptomyces*/bacterium

   (b) (i) So that only a single species/strain is used to prepare the inoculums
         or idea of pure culture
         or uncontaminated culture

      (ii) Area X

   (c) dissolve oxygen/aerate
      or to achieve distribution of nutrients/fungal cells/heat energy/efficient mixing

   (d) *Any one from:*
      filtration/ultrafiltration
      addition of salt to a penicillin rich solvent
      precipitation from solvent/flocculation
      centrifugation
      crystallisation

   (e) production starts as glucose is (nearly) exhausted
      or lag period 0-1.5 days before production begins

      production begins towards end of active growth/exponential phase
      or production begins as stationary phase is entered/growth plateaus

2. (a) *Any two from:*
      Mouse injected with antigens
      Production of B-cells triggered/activated
      (B-cells) isolated from spleen

   (b) Polyethylene glycol/PEG

   (c) *Any one from:*
      • mAbs bind to cancer cell-specific antigens
      • immune response against target cancer cell triggered
        or body destroys its own cancer cells
      • delivery of radiation directly to tumours (radioactive molecule can be attached to mAb)
      • delivery of attached toxin to destroy cancer cell
      • treatment of breast cancer using herceptin
      • mAb can prevent growth of cancer cells (by blocking growth receptors)

3. 1. cell walls reduce yield
   2. composition/component: pectin, cellulose, araban
   3. cellulose tough/causes difficulty with breaking open cells
      or cellulose makes mechanical extraction difficult
   4. pectin increases viscosity/causes difficulty with filtration
   5. pectin/araban cause haze/cloudiness
   6. first example of enzyme used to break down the wall materials (see list below)
   7. second example (see list below)
   8. low solubility issues of araban and pectin

   Examples
   Cellulose breaks down cellulose/increases yield
   Pectinase breaks down pectin/decreases viscosity/decreases haze
   Arabanase breaks down araban/decreases haze

4. (a) Living cells only

   (b) (i) 1.25% and 2.5%
      (ii) same initial concentration of colony forming units/same viable count added to each dilution
      (iii) 9 million cells

Section C: Animal Behaviour

1. (a) (i) 15
      (ii) *Any one from:*
         they break more easily/less (total) height needed to break them
         it takes fewer drops to break them
         shorter handling time
         less time/energy to break shells

   (b) optimal foraging maximises net energy gain

      it gives the lowest **total** height needed to break a whelk
      the least energy expenditure in flight at this height

      or

   (c) Encounter rate (of prey by predator)/search time

2. 1. nature = behaviour that is innate/instinct/genetically determined
      or
      nature allows stereotyped response to stimuli
   2. nurture defined as behavioural modification/learning
   3. nature eg: any example of instinctive behaviour
   4. nurture eg: imprinting/habituation/cultural transmission
      or description of species and behaviour
   5. (adult) invertebrates generally have a shorter **lifespan** than primates *
   6. long lifespan gives time for learning
   7. short lifespan entails reliance on innate behaviour
      or
      invertebrates rely on innate behaviour
   8. invertebrate **parental care** is rare *
   9. primates rely more on **nurture than do invertebrates**
   * converse applies

3. (a) (i) *Any two from:*
         Healthy females produce many eggs
         Brood pouch filled faster/reduced mating time
         Reduced predation risks
         Increase in number of eggs fertilised
      (ii) *Any one from:*
         Genes allow more copies to pass into next generation
         Genes more likely to be passed on to next generation
         Genes are self-preserving
         Genes assist survival of the male fish

(b) *Any one from:*
Nutrition of young in brood pouch/carrying young
Providing parental care

(c) Males do not avoid other males with black spots

(d) Fish with solvent only

(e) Males are not influenced by displays/stimuli that females might show if they saw the males

4. (a) (On average) they share half of their genes/genetic material
or The chances of sharing a gene are 0.5/50%

(b) (i) Genes for altruism will spread when rB–C>0
or
helping relatives is beneficial when rB–C>0

(ii) (Three) groups of most related have highest cannibalism
or
no correlation

Section C: Physiology, Health and Exercise

1. 1. deposition of fatty materials/plaque forms/atheroma forms
2. (atheroma) **under** lining layer/endothelium/intima **of artery**
3. platelets attach to rough surface/platelets release clotting factors
or thrombus/clot forms at site of plaque
4. clot/embolus/atheroma can block/narrow vessel
5. **blockage** of <u>coronary artery</u>
6. heart muscle cells **die** beyond blockage
or heart muscle cells **die** from lack of oxygen

2. (a) **increase** exercise
reduce intake of fatty foods

(b) (i) <u>5.9</u> (mmol/l)
(ii) *Any two from:*
LDL has been reduced (to 2.9)/LDL now within normal range
Total cholesterol is reduced/now about normal
Total cholesterol/HDL ratio reduced/now about normal
(iii) 32.7% **or** (about) 33%

3. (a) pancreas/islets/Beta cells **detect** glucose **and** insulin secretion (increases)

(Glucose level is reduced when)
cells in liver/muscle/adipose tissue (increase) uptake glucose
or
glucose is converted to/stored as glycogen

(b) (i) fewer receptors active/functioning/responding to insulin
or
receptors do not recruit glucose transporters to the membrane

(ii) obesity is cause (of insulin resistance/Type 2 diabetes)

high W:H/this ratio is an indicator for obesity
(so worth reducing it)
or
(reducing ratio) will reduce obesity/BMI

4. (a) (Sporting activities) increase bone mass/bone density/bone mineral density (BMD)
or
osteoporosis takes longer to develop because BMD is higher

greatest bone mass achieved when young/by age of 30/in adolescence
or
gives higher BMD before age-related loss

(b) (i) These are most common fracture sites in elderly/those with osteoporosis

(ii) not a weight bearing exercise and allows comparison with the others
or
to demonstrate that **only** weight bearing exercise is effective

(iii) (Sample data eg)
size of sample, replication
variation in BMD/age between subjects
idea of measuring error, eg error bars

Hey! I've done it

BrightRED
PUBLISHING

© 2011 SQA/Bright Red Publishing Ltd, All Rights Reserved
Published by Bright Red Publishing Ltd, 6 Stafford Street, Edinburgh, EH3 7AU
Tel: 0131 220 5804, Fax: 0131 220 6710, enquiries: sales@brightredpublishing.co.uk,
www.brightredpublishing.co.uk

Official SQA answers to 978-1-84948-228-8
2007-2011